2 Love Her No More!

2 Love Her No More!

The Superhero Lover's Saga Continues

Shaun Saunders

Shaun Saunders
Atlanta, Georgia

Contents

Foreword

Relevant, necessary, powerful, awe-inspiring, educator, father, husband, spiritual leader are all descriptors of the dynamic Shaun S. Saunders. Add author to the list of accolades and the plot thickens. The writings predecessor sets the stage for heat, lust, and raw unbridled passion. The Superhero Lover is every woman's fantasy. When the answer to what our (women's') bodies desire meets up with the answer to our lustful prayers the result can be quite unpredictable. Our childhood perceptions of the definition of love are challenged by adult needs and idealized notions of Mr. and Mrs. Right. 2 *Love Her No More* picks up where the prequel leaves off and is an honest visual inside the lives of couples when the honeymoon phase fizzles out. He boldly takes us through the phases that love can bring and fearlessly expresses what most of us feel but are not necessarily prepared to admit to ourselves or share with our partners. Each chapter is representative of thoughts that are not readily revealed. From

My Companion, My Friend, and My Enemy to Picture Perfect, your thoughts and emotions are challenged or validated by the poignant expressions of honesty.

Saunders' style of writing is forward, raw, gritty, and quite frankly sexy! He dares to challenge the status quo of what some may feel is how a man of God should express himself. His style goes against the grain of a spiritual leader which makes us more compelled to read and fall in love with his work.

It has been stated that people come into your life for a reason, a season, or a lifetime. It has been a pleasure to become acquainted with such a dynamic man. It has enlivened my spirit to be a part of the fruits of the labor of Saunders and his beautiful wife. Their children are the epitome of love, devotion, and high expectations. I strongly urge you to not only read this book, but take time to discuss and share with your loved ones. It's definitely a conversation starter.

Nikki Glover

Introduction

Ladies and Gentlemen, He's Backkkk! To an audience eagerly intrigued with a contagious curiosity, determined to see what the end is going to be in the Superhero Lover's love chronicles, the saga continues with the details that motivated his decision to either forever love, the Sexy and Vivacious Mrs. Destiny, or to love her no more. The question of whether it is love that he was feeling, or if it is the love that he had been searching for is the foundation upon which the Superhero will present the thesis of his conclusion as a means to rationalize for himself and subliminally compel the empathy of others to appreciate the inevitability of whatever his choice will be.

Under the misguided notion that love was the highest pinnacle on which their relationship could stand, denying the reality of love's impossibility when left to fend for itself in an atmosphere infused with the ignorance of the unlearned, Mr. Lover Man, no not Shabba Ranks, has unsuspectingly become the epitome of a relationship vigilante. From the sweltering Alleghenies, where he was once overwhelmingly nominated for the illustrious Nobel Peace Prize for his revitalization of the declining esteem for the Godly man as a sure foundation in the infrastructure of the family core, to the appalling posture of disgrace that characterizes the wimp in every man, the Superhero has come to that relationship crossroad, where he must decide if his train will remain on the tracks or if he would rather choose for it to be derailed.

Challenged by the assumption that he has little to no time left before his caboose tragically collides with his bride's runaway train, influenced by the current conditions of his environment, he seeks out an exit strategy that will enable him to dismiss himself from his many-layered levels of accountability, when determining his contribution to the collision that rocked their marriage. With an overwhelming disdain for the winter season, the Superhero Lover rebels against the current seasonal conditions by putting on clothing that exposes the fragility of his vulnerability, instead of covering up his bare necessities from the frigidness of an extremely cold climate. With the pride of his shamed masculinity succumbing to the blistering wounds of his severely frostbitten ego, the Superhero leaps head first into the deep end of an ocean filled with the unruly waves of his emotions overtaking him in his self-proclaimed isolated sea of regret. Now shivering frantically, naively running to play outside in the snow in his drawers, absent the convenient apparel of his gloves and his little Superhero snow boots, the uncertainty of their love for which he was initially convinced he knew has caused his heart to go into cardiac arrest due to the crowning of love's impossibility that has forcefully seated itself down on the throne of his unruly emotions. As he struggles within himself, questioning in the words of Dru Hill, "What are we going to do, what are we going say, where are we going to go when they find out," he retreats into the corner of his brokenheartedness with instructors coaching him to heavily consider separation and even divorce as the most reasonable alternatives. Weighed down with a retrospective posture that constantly contemplates how things would have been different, if he would have done this instead of that, the thin line, he chose to walk across, roped tightly to the towers of love and hate has ferociously buckled causing him to fall into the disappointment of love's pit without the security of a safety net to cushion his fall.

Seeing their marriage now plunge into the deep and unchartered territories, of what for most has been a one-way journey with very little to no promise of return, the Superhero grabs for any available crutch left to save him from this death-defying fall. When falling, however, sometimes Superhero's have a tendency to grab hold of things that expedite their dive into the deep depths of their shark-infested ocean rather than grabbing hold of those things that will secure their climb out of their cave of isolation. Instead of grabbing hold of God's word the Superhero grabs hold to the addictions of porn. His lusty eyes are enticed by the sexual appeal of the female anatomy accompanied by the afflicted self-gratification of masturbation, only showing a resistance, at times, to temptation because of sin's patience to present him with the most favorable opportunity to participate in the deceitfulness of its promised pleasure. With blinded eyes, disguising a lack of opportunity with the posture of his overly indulgent self-proclaimed deliverance promotional tour, the Superhero Lover is pressured by the ferocious waves of his own insecurities that have imprisoned him in his adolescence. Even in role modelish presentation of the Superhero's masculine masculinity, the lack of harmony within himself regarding the inadequacies of his maleness will always cause him to jeopardize the integrity of his manhood.

Now stuck at that place where the initial contact with his abominable affliction first occurred during the immaturity of his adolescence, like most men the appearance of the Superhero's masculine posture is the deceptive measure used to qualify his evolution from the inherited posture of maleness into the accepted responsibility of manhood. This deceptive presumption that misleadingly suggests manhood is the inevitable crowning of maleness as the sole heir to become the man anointed to sit on humanities throne, without the dedication of pledging and legal crossing over into its fraternal order, has caused males to recklessly submit themselves to a delusional idea of automatic entitlement. Manhood, however, is not an automatic in the natural maturation of a maleness biologically inherited, but rather the highest pinnacle of a matured male's postured evolution that enables him to consciously put forth an undeniable effort to willingly embrace the responsibility of a designated office, man, without having to compromise the integrity of his character. It is imperative for every male earnestly aspiring to be a man to respectfully accept the daunting reality that yes, every man is a male, but not every male is a man.

Manhood is not the fulfilled promise of entitlement to those fortunate enough to inherently occupy the office of maleness, but a privilege to males responsible enough to courageously stand strong under the burdensome plight placed on the male man. The biologically inherited unchecked lust, developed in the innocence and immaturity of adolescents, are the oppositional proclivities that emasculate males from the nature of their masculinity, which in turn causes them to neglect the responsibility of their manhood.

Now, as a result of being convinced he must squabble in isolation with a lust that continues to express itself through the corrupted flesh of his male ancestral genealogy, the Superhero seeks, like Adam, to politely dismiss his inner hoe from the history of his story without ever passing the graduation exit exam to validate his matriculation from Mr. Naughty to Mr. Lover Nice. The Superhero Lover, misguided by the notion that the incredible beauty of her attraction at the genesis of their ecstasy would inevitably remain an immutable constant throughout the duration of their relationship, is conflicted within himself about how to respond to the absent continuity of the reflection of the sexy hot momma he was for sure she would always and forever be.

Like most deceived men, the Superhero initiates most of his contact with love on the premise of a moment in ecstasy's time that enabled him to unrealistically surrender himself over to the ignorance of an idea that caused him to fall in love with a photographic image of her that he captured in the newness of a beautiful moment they etched in time. Unfortunately, the allusive presumption of that stilled photo of her unblemished presentation became the idol of an expectation that never accounted for the silence of her beast patiently waiting for the right time to reveal itself through the pores of her impeccable flawed presentation. In other words, love should never be measured or wholeheartedly trusted to continue always to be what it appeared to be when it first knocked on your door, but rather be measured by the admirable admonishing and extreme sensitivity towards the oftentimes neglected beast that accompanies its beauty.

As *Their World Turns*, throughout the course of the *Days of Their Lives*, and the seemingly unbearable difficulties of marriage have them questioning their choice as they learn how to tolerate each other throughout the years of the *Young and the Restless*, the Sexy and Vivacious Mrs. Destiny cries out, like Prince in *Purple Rain*, to her Superhero Lover, "Do you want her, or do you want me, because I want you oho ohoo?" Really, could it be that the Superhero's unhealthy cravings for a Candy Girl he assumed would rock his world, have prompted him to suspend his organically regimented diet, manufactured specifically for his satisfaction, in exchange for the inevitable catastrophe that accommodates the infidelity of mingling with a new sexy kept on standby? After 7-10 years of marriage, has his love, conflicted by the fanatical allure of the voluptuously sexy seduction of his well-figured mistress, decided to change its mind after questioning Mrs. Destiny's ability to abide by the conditions his love required for her, at the beginning of their relationship to uphold? After the love is gone and what used to be right now feels so wrong, will the Lovers break up to make up or will the Superhero Lover choose to love her or love her no more?

I (the Superhero), therefore announce that in the case of "The Superhero Lover: He Loves Me or He Loves Me No More," File Number 1119673, that when it comes to loving you or loving you not no more, I announce that I, that I choose to, to, to …....................!

My Companion, My Friend, And My Enemy

Session Six

"Even My close friend, someone I trusted, one who shared my bread, has turned against me."
(Psalm 41:9, NIV)

The absurdity of one's fabricated assumption with a luminous idea of what most would violently oppose love is not, continues to be the controversial theory investigated through a model called companionship, the recognized testing ground upon which the integrity of this theory's success and failure is measured. A companion is one of a pair or set of things; a mate. A companion is supposed to be esteemed as someone needed and possessed with an inherent fortitude to care and be cared for by a worthy suitor in desperate need of services only he or she is equipped to provide. In

Genesis chapter two, God speaks to the awkwardness He declares would inevitably accompany the loneliness of a man being left alone: to exist in isolation, to be kept in the company of oneself, or to live in the absence of a sufficient help necessary for man to successfully adhere to a request that would confirm the purpose of his existence. Therefore, God made Eve, the good and needed thing who willfully relinquished all rights to care for herself, not because she could not, over to the responsibility of Adam, the man in desperate need of her services. Under the notion that Ms. Destiny, like a paramedic called to the scene of an accident, would be able to acclimate her needed services under the umbrella of conditions God predetermined necessary to stabilize the continuity of his existence, and that her sense of understanding of when and where to apply pressure to the wounds of his insecurities guaranteeing a full recovery of his life, the Superhero, for reasons unknown until now, has called into question the civility of her companionship.

With this line of thinking serving as the logic of his reasoning, the Superhero Lover moves to make his first public statement since the exposure of those clear-cut details he shared with us about his explicit behavior with Mrs. Destiny in between the sheets, in this the 6th session penned in the journal of his love chronicles entitled, *My Companion, My Friend, and My Enemy.*

Opening to an audience filled with reporters, former flames and past desires, haters, and appreciators, ready to explain those matters that have influenced the logical or illogical rationale he's decided to stand on as it pertains to his choice; he proceeds with his processional down the road of explanation with an awkward question he poses to only the invited few residing in the press room, that at first appears to be irrelevant to the topic of discussion.

"How many of you have or are thinking about purchasing a house?"

The press wondered why, with the all the media attention centered around this press conference, why in the hell he would choose to ask any question as opposed to immediately offering a straight, clearly followable line of thinking. In response to what at the time an attentively engaged press seemed to consider to be a question with absolutely no relevance whatsoever regarding the circumstances surrounding the moment, the Daily Times Most Diabolical Reporter, the accuser of the brethren, sarcastically responds with, "Yes I am looking, and it just so happens that one of the reasons why I am here is because I was coming to check up on the availability of yours, since it appears that the beauty of your house on the outside was a cover used to disguise the absence of a home on the inside." A flurry of oooooooohs rests on the tongues of reporters in the room, laughing uncontrollably at another one of the Times Diabolical Reporter's classic insulting attacks on the Superhero Lover. The Superhero surprisingly, however, to the reporter's dismay, laughs along with the press, dismissing the air of ignorance in the room with a hint of his own sarcasm to counter their traditional dogma with an oddity that reengages their adventurous capacity of wonder.

"Now that I have your full attention, please allow me to proceed. As you know, for those of you privileged to purchase either of the two, a house or a car, there are guidelines and questions most people ask themselves while considering the returnable profit they expect to accommodate their investment. When looking for a house, the first questions we ask is, where do I want to live. The environment in which we choose to live must be welcoming, with conditions easily acclimatable and nurtured with a natural order of appreciation for your gifts and the gifts of those who accompany you.

Next, it is imperative for you to decide on your purchasing option: Do you want to lease, lease to buy, or are you going to purchase?

Some of us like to keep our options open just in case things do not work out; you know what I mean. Now that we have done these two things, it is time for you to check on the availability of houses in the area you want to live in. It is, however, extremely important that you, at this point, do not preoccupy yourself with the potential availability of a house that is already occupied. Eliminate all possibility for conflict of interest. You must make sure nobody else is scheduled to live in that house at the same time you are. Finally, you must determine how much you are willing to pay for your house. How much is it worth to you? Do you have the resourcefulness to continuously meet the demand of the cost for the house and ensure the appreciation of it worth?

So, what purpose do houses and cars play in my defense? Interestingly enough looking for a place to live or a car to drive is similar in theory to searching for a suitable companion. The first question, where do I want to live when it comes to companionship, speaks specifically to the acclimation of oneself under an umbrella of the mandatory conditions needed to ensure the continuity of your companion's existence and/or survival. Before you choose to give yourself away, you should always check to see if the atmospheric conditions your prospective suitor has decided to reside in are capable, at the highest level, of securely accommodating the safety of your needed contribution, absent the possibility of any form of collusion and without ever warranting adjustments that might cause you to compromise your integrity. Like any home buyer, the environment you choose to live in may be riddled with toxic bullets that gradually increase the odds of your fatality, rather than the unspeakable joy that follows the fulfillment of life in longevity. When you have carefully tested for contamination and determined the toxic levels of the prospective atmosphere you can see yourself thriving in to be acceptable; you must then decide how long you plan on staying.

The leasing option shows an unwillingness to commit, always keeping your options open to the potential of renewal with a legally binding guarantee centered around a litany of illegal month-to-month relations that falsely award marital privileges to the immaturity of the compromisingly uncommitted. In this case, after you have served your 6 to 12-month sentence, you tend to move on to whatever you assume to be better next, jumping from one relationship to another, afraid of closeness and its relationship with its best friend, vulnerability. Individuals pursuing after these kinds of relations usually walk away without submitting their 2-week notice or they continue to make unannounced conjugal visits to the property, entering in with the privileges of a friend and exiting with the benefits of one of many lovers. Unfortunately, in either of the two outcomes, the house continues to depreciate in market value.

The next option, Lease to Buy, shows the promise of longevity and commitment, with no guarantee, on the terms of one's sensual perception, determining the potential quality of its fruit only after smelling, tasting, and touching the virginity of his or her innocence. In this context most people associate the act of sex to be a direct correlation of love's expression, selling their souls for a feel of an orgasmic moment in exchange for their birthed right. The most common form of logic that follows this line of thinking lives by statements that imply an openness of trying on relationships to see how they fit on you without any consideration for the wear and tear of your oversized ego on the worth of your prospective lover. The tendency of giving too much too soon, classifying the terms of your agreement with impulsively endearing titles such as "Girlfriend" and "Boyfriend," names that equip suitors with a false sense of entitled rights to what they legally have no right to, has caused people to place the demand of 'the one for me' on the shoulders of unqualified individuals God only brought to them to be a friend, supporter, motivator, encourager, acquaintance, or even a soul in desperate need of hearing about a Savior. Just like with the lease to buy option when dealing with an acquisition of a home, most pursuers of a loving relationship who choose this option rarely ever purchase the rights to the home.

The last of these three housing acquisitions, the purchasing option, is the most sincerely calculated display of investment revealing the unexplainable depths of love's uncompromising commitment, without any reluctance or fear of the unknown, to ruthlessly meet the demand of the relationship's cost with unyielding confidence in love's profitable return. This kind of investor goes all in, reconnecting again with the memory of the one God saw fit to previously acquaint him or her with before time, and with one look, regaining full consciousness from the hypnosis of sins amnesiac stupor, declares like

Adam upon waking up from his deep sleep, "Finally I found the suitable helper my soul has been longing for." In this relational context, the rigorous study to know the strengths and weaknesses wrestling within one another in the psychological filter of one's mind, and the acquisitions of gathered data revealing the needed TLC your prospective companion would need from you to cure the dysfunction that deceitfully obscures the unmeasurable value of their home, are the most transformational God logic most of the world, unfortunately, continues to reject.

Now it is finally time for you to choose a house. Remember, however, when choosing, not to preoccupy yourself with the availability of a house that is already occupied. Is it not rude to pursue after a date with someone who already has a date? Today, people ruthlessly move in to stake their claim and right to pursue after dates with happily and unhappily married men and women without guilt or remorse for the consequences of their actions. The ignorant understanding of availability often leads to covetousness, the illegal trespassing on the premises of a companion's property, a companion God specifically mandated to be a suitable helper for another, not you, He determined to be worthy of that other person's services. Sometimes liking a house that is empty at the moment can cause you to covet the companion of which the legal recipient of his or her love, still traveling through time's GPS, is searching to find that one house God destined to be his or her home. It is imperative that I insert here that some people already have homes and look to purchase additional properties (e.g., vacation homes, timeshares, etc.) These properties are usually purchased for a fun time, leisurely activities, time away from the main house, you know your main girl to engage in the fantasy of relations with no consequential expectations. The flirtatiously dirty, dirty dancing routine all too common in the tragedy of extramarital concubine escapades undermines the unmeasurable value and worth of the homely house for the depreciating unloyalty of a promiscuous hoe's (male or female) hotel room.

The illusion of professionally trimmed grass appears to be greener on that side based on an obscured fanatical observation from a distance. The interest, intrigue, and preoccupation with the resonating glory of the beautifully cut grass landscaping another house that seduces your lust is only a distraction causing homeowners to get bit by the snakes they can't see slithering in the yard of their uncut grass. Unfortunately, in this relationship, a house can never become a home. Although the homeowner is heavily invested in the relationship, after some time the newness of the acquisition wears off, and the lust of their loins bears more influence on them than the intellect of their spiritual logic, causing them in tough times to run away to a temporary place to play with toys they found in another yard.

Lastly, the determination of your house purchase must always conclude with the utmost consideration for this question: Do you have within you the resourcefulness to continue throughout time to meet the costly demand of the purchase price for the house to become a home? In other words, are you possessed with the will, ingenuity, strength, patience, unconditional love, knowledgeable application of love, wisdom, desire, passion, trust, compromise, openness, unmeasurable depths of forgiveness, and the God heart to care for your companion the way God intended for them to be cared for? Most people opt-in and buy into relationships they like without carefully calculating

throughout time the continuity of the relationship demands and their ability and/or willingness to pay the cost, in full, of the purchase price
they agreed to. I have learned that you better
make sure never to write a check that your
a……….. can't cash, because that is a debt that
will generate an almost insurmountable interest
that will imprison the creative monster of the
progeny you hope will continue on your legacy.

My purpose for using analogies, paraboli-
cally, above in my comparisons of purchasing
a house with the selection of a suitable companion, was intended to create a realm of continued
openness that would allow newcomers and acquaintances familiar with Mrs. Destiny and my
relations to objectively review the details of my
witness before prematurely rendering against
me a guilty verdict. It also upholds the integrity
of a mantra that many seekers of companionship
know they are supposed to live by, but because
of their daunting admiration with the rhythm of
their pace as they step in the name of love, they
naively permit it to lie dormant under the radar
of their non-negotiable relationship. I knew, but
overlooked, the importance of understanding
how the unmeasurable beauty of us being lovers

depended on the immutability of a covenant witnessed in the innocent imperfections of the lost and misunderstood art of Friendship.

Because we became friends second, demanding each other to live up to an unrealistic idea of love first, we missed out on maturing our communication with fidelity's partner, Friendship, the missing ingredient in our relational sauce that would have privileged us with the freedom of exposing our imperfections absent the ignorant presumptions of prejudice. See within the corridors of friendship lies the admirable appreciation and recognition for a persons' innocents while they at times masquerade immaturely around in the dirty dust of their anatomy's imperfections. This would have exposed us both to the unrestricted messy versions of us, cradling the secrecy of our vulnerabilities in the protective grasp of friendship's honesty, without the guilty shame of our self-inflicted offenses and the offenses committed against us by our offenders. Not only should friendship precede companionship, but the continuity of its progressive existence is the imperative mantra that if not abided by can catastrophically disrupt the rhythm of love's beating heart. It is a must for us that friendship not be considered as exclusive, relevant only in the pursuit of companionship, but rather a stream of living water that continues to flow after conquering and capturing the innocence of the objective we have aggressively pursued. Now I realize after all this time struggling to rediscover the innocence of God's perfection working in me that the innocence of me could only be perceived through the pores of my dirty, dirty, dusty imperfect anatomy which I mistakenly assumed your love, Mrs. Destiny, without the sufficiency of your friendship, would certainly be enough to embrace my fragile frame.

What we should have or could have done, looking back through those thick butt bifocal lenses better known as hindsight, is of no relevance in terms of what we are going to do now with regard to where we currently stand. Knowing now that the foundation of friendship is a mandatory ingredient needed in every romantic relational recipe, so that couples, later on down the road, should not have to become the friends for each other they should have already been, is important and at the same time invaluable since we skipped over that step before arriving at this destination. After turning on love's fire and desire, b-a-b-y, just like the infamous Rick James and Tina Marie, how do we extinguish the flames of the fire we made, with the unlit match of friendship, the anointed oil that can ensure the eternity of our lover's burn? Is it even possible for us to believe in the innocence of friendships promise, after being stabbed in the heart multiple times with a companion's offensive, knife of offenses? Yes, in the words of Bobby Valentino, we were supposed to be best friends, instead of playing house warped in the emotionally illegal entitlements of a boyfriend and a girlfriend swallowing up the privileges without the more adorable luxury of the promise.

The question then is how do you become best friends with a companion, stained with an unlawfully bitter resentment against you, who reacts to you more like an enemy rather than a friend? Or how can we, after being submerged in the presence of love's garden of Eden, that spot on Earth for a moment where love is an open door to the romantic heavens where we presume God destined for the two of us to be, master the art of becoming friends after years of sleeping around with each other as enemies?

You were supposed to be my lover, my companion, and my best friend, but now it seems as if I have become the punching bag for the show-stopping arrival of an enemy's wrath I still don't understand, causing me to reconsider the reason why I Would Die for You. By no means am I an angel, but neither am I the devil that you sometimes portray me to be. See, honestly, I never meant to cause you any problems and never meant to cause you any pain, because I adore you! But you, with your silent dismissal of our partnership, an absurdly ridiculous obsession with prioritizing the insignificance of others at the expense of my own significance, and either your unwillingness or your inability to apply the necessary medicine to relieve me from the bloody wound of an insecurity you know and see is causing me excruciating pain, has nullified for me your promise that until the end of time, you would be here for me. Girl, your beast has blinded me to the internal beauty I still see resonating through the pores of your posterior, projecting publicly the politically correct posture of a good wife, but displaying privately an unfathomable decadence that eliminates any guarantee of the oneness we vowed we would share.

Like Thomas Jefferson, you convey in the declaration of our relational interdependence a Paradox of Liberty that admonishes an attitude of submission to me, your supposed worthy suitor, while in the same breath defending society's newly advanced aberration of your woman's right to headship through the emasculation of my manly needs by demanding I follow in line with the malicious desires of a two-headed monster staggering under the hypnosis of your direction. To this notion of your arrogance, fueled by your ignorance, you cheerfully applaud the pulseless beat of my dead heart, declaring in the words of Ralph Tresvant that you need a man with sense-i-ti-vi-ty, while all the time contradicting this logic with an illogically rational presumption that causes you to challenge my manhood's strength when confronted by the cunning craftiness of a subtle serpent that continues to trespass illegally in the grass of our secret garden. It took some time, but finally I realize that all along we have had an open marriage, intrigued by the premeditated gratification we expected to accompany several countless ménage à trois encounters, to which we ignorantly conceded the innocence of our logic over to the emotionalism of our undisciplined loins, with the skeptically illusive interjections of a slithering serpent. It appears through these miscalculated costly acts of infidelity that we lost ourselves, deceived into believing we were saving each other from an abrasive ocean undercurrent that was simultaneously drowning the both of us. We're still drowning, sinking in the underbelly of a surge of violent waves that have submerged us in unchartered waters infested with the disappointment of our emotional wounds spilling the blood of our broken hearts into an ocean filled with schools of piranha and hungry sharks.

I remember when our hearts broke and we, because of our circumstances—the circle we created for ourselves to stand in—privately became enemies while covering up for others the lies of our imperfections with an imposturous public display of affections deceitfully communicated through the insincere motions of our Academy award-winning performances in our hit movie entitled "My Companion and My Friend." I remember when I almost gave up on loving you, but I decided, even after I knew the love between us was gone, to stay, hoping you would leave so that I could blame you for giving up first on what I thought I had already given up on. For a long time, we have tried to smile, but the muscles in our faces refuse to allow us to exercise that expression of jubilee, all because we captured one another's bodies, without ever calculating the cost for winning over each other's soul: our minds, our wills, and our emotions. You once asked, "To what extent was I willing to love you too and at what point in our relationship will my love for you decide to walk away, stop, or cease to exist for you my companion; my friend; and my enemy?" This may surprise you, but amidst all that we have been through, and all that I have tried to do within my power to escape your whip appeal on me, I just can't, I can't stop loving you! Do you remember just how good, good love between us can be?

The questions then that we should be asking has nothing to do with me loving you or loving you no more, but rather if I were to choose this time to ask: Do you think you possess within you the depth of a submissive will, to which you will humbly obey, when God commands for you to SHUT UP AND LET ME LOVE YOU? Do you?

Shut Up and Let Me Love You

Session Seven

Husbands, love your wives, as Christ loved the church and gave Himself up for her, that He might sanctify her, having cleansed her by the washing of water with the word, so that He might present the church to Himself in splendor, without spot or wrinkle or any such thing, that she might be holy and without blemish. In the same way husbands should love their wives as their own bodies. He who loves his wife loves himself. For no one ever hated his own flesh, but nourishes and cherishes it, just as Christ does the church (Ephesians 5:25-29, ESV).

With what appeared to be an excruciatingly painful exhaling breath, relieving her from the emotional turmoil she was certain her ex-lover was about to confirm, Mrs. Destiny is left startled by his answer to a question for which she longed to hear his heart's response, How Do You Love Me?' With his part of the answer resting softly in the grasp of her clutches she is left to decide if committing her soul's worth over to the worthiness of her lover's possessed will is enough for her to shut the hell up and grant God's Love, through him, the right to lead her all the way. Now, wait just a minute! I think I might need to park the car right here for a moment. Ladies, please don't presuppose that the tone of my diction derives from the egotistically misogynistic anatomy of an adolescent smothered in the psychological immaturity of my dirty, dirty, dusty maleness. No, but rather from a more aggressive place dormant on the inside of the passivity of the first Adam, who quietly stood beside Eve as that old subtle serpent deceived her with his sweet talk that caused love in its purest form to experience the agony of shame for the first time. First Timothy 2:13-14 (NASB) explains it like this:

"For it was Adam who was first created, and then Eve. And it was not Adam who was deceived, but the woman being deceived, fell into transgression."

Interestingly, if you listen to hear what the Scripture is not saying, you can clearly hear what it said. The serpent's crafty ability to pontificate radically un-precedented sentiments of skepticism within the psychological process of Eve's central thought, deceitfully massaged the lust of her eyes and flesh to converse in a dialogue with another brother all while the brother she was with was passively standing right beside her. Notice throughout the continuity of Adam and Eve's relational rhythm, love is never considered or even mentioned within the paradigm of their united context. It would, therefore, be an inaccurate assumption for anyone to suggest that the united front that brought the two of them together, did so without the highest level of concern for the absence of love in the purest form of itself, expressed in the natural order of its activity rather than in the shelled emptiness of a posture contained in the allusion of love in word without its affection. More simply, Adam's silence or lack of aggressive contempt towards the attempted assault on Eve, all while openly observing the serpent's premeditated act of offense, is the absence of love's actions speaking up on behalf of the woman he was supposed to defend, watching as she fought to defend herself against an employee subjected to his authority. Love, if it would have been appropriately asserted here in its purest form by Adam, would have intervened as the authorized voice of authority confining Eve, willfully, to the committed posture of the SHUT UP, because of her assurance in the security of her defender's defense.

The context of this story reveals that Eve's passionately impulsive urges to echo the sound of love in word, an action God intended for Adam to bounce off the anatomy of the woman hidden in Eve's female, caused her to naively engage in an adulterous affair, feeling justified in her right to usurp the preeminence of Adam's created order because of his weak display of masculinity's tone during the most crucial moment in the development of her independent thought.

As Samson did with Delilah, Adam's lassitude prematurely exposed an unlocked door to the sensitive areas of his vulnerabilities, encouraging the immature psychosis of Eve's estranged witness to parade around in the delicacy of her femininity wearing the unoccupied mask of Adam's/ unclaimed masculinity. The silence of Adam's word unspoken speaks louder to Eve's demise than the supposed disillusionment with which others suggest she was deceived. Though it appears she was deceived, the question we must ask is what is it that Adam did, or did not do that caused her to flirt around with such ominous deceit. As most women would, Mrs. Destiny upon her Lover pilot's first attempt to land this controversial philosophy, THE SHUT UP, on the runway of her heart, moves to protest what she initially perceives as an extremely deplorable form of sexual harassment. Though the echoing sentiments of THE SHUT UP theory resonate predictably well in an arena of male pilots traditionally summoned to the control of a man only cockpit and the expected subservient submissiveness of all female stewards, it's clear for Mrs. Destiny and women all across the world, upon first hearing its request, that THE SHUT UP poises an offensive, misogynistic arrogance that threatens their womanly preservation and freedom of equality.

As a result of being offended, Mrs. Destiny campaigns aggressively for the votes of women worldwide to elect her to the office of chief spokeswoman trumping the illogically radical momentum of an extremist women's rights movement. Like Donald Trump, she moves with an unorthodox disdain, vehemently intent on MAKING WOMEN GREAT AGAIN, rallying women from all backgrounds to violently protest all the fake news media outlets that respect the institution of THE SHUT UP and its administration. With supporters of the movement rallying together awaiting the state of the women's union address, a speech laced in the reciprocal perverseness of an inverted misogyny fused with the colorful stereotypical dogma passionately jargoned this time through the offended zeal of women, Mrs. Destiny is greeted with an overwhelming applause of jovial celebration as she approaches the podium, accompanied by the craftiness of that subtle serpent cheerleading her all the way down the yellow brick road. Now standing amidst a crowd, full of rebellious women LIT ALL THE WAY UP, Mrs. Destiny feeds off the explicit vulgarity of a menacing militia hyping up the naivety of a disgruntled group of offended Eves as she proceeds to rock the mic. But like a powerful impact BOOM, BOOM from her Superhero Lover's canon, precisely timed to explode right at the moment Mrs. Destiny was scheduled to speak her first word, the sound of unified men, led by her former hero, come marching down all around the walls of their supposed fortified city shouting in the authoritative voices of their absent warrior defenders, "SHUUUUUUUUUUT UPPPPPP, AND LET ME LOVE YOUUUUUUU!

As the reemergent sound of Adam's Man Power drowns the regressively undisciplined appetite of his infidelious passivity, the echoing confidence of rediscovering his once emasculated masculinity, simultaneously turns the heads of a volatile group of independent women ready to spearhead, at the expense of all male casualties, a 21st Century heiress revolution. All the women, with murderous thoughts, move to confront the ignorance of their male offenders in a flanked formation. Accompanied by the illusion of a seductive pop and bounce of their most provocative extremities, they are intent like Sharon Stone in *"Basic Instinct"* on binding each man's soul with a projected fantasy of love and then stabbing them in the heart with an ice pick they hid behind their backs.

Assuming these warrior men, gathered to protest their revolt, would be unable to resist the aggressions of their lusty nymphomaniac, to the women's surprise none of the men are hypnotized by the spell cast by the evilness of their witch attempts to castrate all the exaggerated evidence to erases the existence of every man's male genitals through the ignorance of their irrational philosophical New World Order. Filled with rage and an uncontrollable fury as a result of their failed attempt to reciprocate the more orthodox version of a Chi Raq protest, women surrender themselves over to the whorish personality of the freak in a fantasy fabricated in the unchecked misogyny of every mans perverted mind. The massive congregation of women participating in the rally maneuver from a ruthless arrogance into the undisclosed details of a B plan they thought the perfection of their A plan would have never caused them ever to have to consider.

In an effort to regain some leverage, asserting that this unannounced uppercut to the chin that caused the knees of a woman's cancerous masculinity that ruthlessly continues to intrude on the premises of her insecure femininity to buckle, the ladies line up in that Alabama and their momma's Louisiana Queen

Beyoncé's unified formational lemonade defensive stance. Ready, locked, and loaded, displaying a confidently poised posture, the rebels in the luxury of immutability move with precision determined never to allow a man to be the cause for why their change should come. Persuaded by the seared wounds of a scornful resentment, they cry out loudly, "From now on its just me, myself, and I. We see no reason why we will ever need a man to lead us again." Thinking the unified ferocity of their toned declaration would undoubtedly convince the opposition to throw up the red flag and surrender their all of me over to their little girl's non-negotiable demands, these women arrogantly turn, presuming this discussion was over because they let their fat ladies sing, only to be serenaded by the gospel of their men bouncing the protest of their disdain of the hardness of their little ladies stony hearts, once more with controversial song, "SHUT UP AND LET ME LOVE YOU!"

No longer shamed by the significance of his absence in the fanatical reality of her current position, the Superhero Lover, the Superhero Team's leader, quickly moves to reaffirm his confident comfort in the fullness of the equipped man he wasn't when his lady love needed him to be. Caught off guard by the undeniable evidence that confirms the mature existence of the man suspect the ladies never suspected their males could be, the Superhero Lover speaks peace into the cantankerous belly of every proud woman's emotional hurricane, intoxicating their souls with the following words fermented through the convicious grapes of real love's strong drink:

"All the ladies in the building, if you can hear me you need to shut up and listen up! For far too long the deafening silence of my masculinity has been usurped by your little girl unforgivingly defending the defenseless valued worth of the phenomenal women your fathers should have affirmed. Marginalized, in the absent reality of every little girl's need to hear her father's' affirmative thoughts, echoing over his daughter the reverberating sound of a woman's worth God previously acquainted you with, you pop your hips with the seductive switch of a revolutionary ready to slay a stage that has traditionally for years demanded you to submit your all of me over to the unethical supremacy of a governing male dictatorship. The ignorance of my maleness has covered all the outer extremities of your body with sexist affiliated tattoos that portray "men" as the hated antagonists you needed to eliminate from your story to ensure it ends peacefully. Under the erroneously delusional assumption that the continuity of your Queen's legacy depends on the expulsion of your King's heirship, you all have prejudicially stereotyped the King in every man by the unfair tragedy of the evil Kings residing in the immaturity of those males that wounded you. Like the silent sound of innocent blood graffitied on the Jim Crowed canvas of every black man's racial profile, gunned down by the ignorance of officers with a favorable advantage rooted in the core of their American white privilege, you pierce the conscience of our souls with the bullets of your rogue words unapologetically echoing the frustrations of your broken heartedness dipped in the fury of your lethargically stereotypical rant screaming, "All *men are heartless cowards, dogs, and sorry excuses for what God qualified a real man should be!"*

So as you stand over top of my wounded frame, smothered up in the flooded gates of my blood spilled all over the ground by the armor piercing bullets shot through the chamber of your damaged heart, you, accompanied by the instigative voices in your head encouraging you, gently press the heated Chrome of your previously fired firearm against the crest of my forehead intent on executing my soul. Here we are, again, at what appears to be the final count-down. With the clicking cock of your gun's hammer and the tapping of your index finger against the trigger, it is imperative that I ask you this one last time, "Do you still love me?" Look at me when I'm talking to you woman! Can you see the beauty of me, the same way, right now? I still admire the beauty of you even while looking at you through the barrel of the gun you have pointed at my head. Before you shoot me, babe, please, please, please! Make sure this is what you really want. If it is or if it's not, I want you to know that I forgive you no matter what you decide. Though it may seem, at this moment, my life is in your hand, you can't take my life, but for you, I will lay it down. I want to let you know I am here with you, at this crossroads, not because you forced me to be, but rather in this place because I chose to be with you.

My ego, my pride, wouldn't allow me to allow you to be the shelter I needed to preserve me from the impending dangers of all my created harm. I never imagined the rib God used to tailor my specially ordered bulletproof vest, designed with the right cushioning to protect the innocence of my heart, would ever become the instrument through which the projectile that might cause my fatality would come. The presumptive thoughts of you, my lady, burdened with the repercussions of my father's failures revealed through the conjuring defiance of my inexcusable weakness, have caused within you an insensitivity towards my inner me, and have regretfully deceived you to ride along, without the safety of my seatbelt, on the rollercoaster looped in the fears of emotional inability. You are the confrontational consequence of my passivity, the lingering residue of a ghost I hid in the unchallenged masculinity of my alter ego's prisoned insecurities, ready to restore the honor of your queen I for years took for granted. At this point now, there is no need or a way for me to convince you of the 'could of and what I would of done' if I knew then what I know now. I can, however, as I lie here staring at you through the loaded barrel of the same gun used to pierce those vital veins and arteries that allow love to flow to and from your heart, say, with the most sincere conviction, totally uninfluenced by whatever you choose to decide, I am so, so, so very sorry!

You're my queen sugar, sugar queen! Lois Lane my Superhero team! The image of beauty never seen, behold the beauty of you my queen!

Just the finest thing to heavenly, I prayed to God
He send you me; captivated by your seduction,
I stand in awe of your excellency. My Destiny,
honored to walk beside you my queen as your
King. A masterpiece specifically created for no
other but me. This is why I can't explain these
feelings that I feel inside; so, let me explain the
reason why. When I look in your eyes, I can
never deny these feelings I'm feeling inside!
My Lady, I am into, I'm so into you! See when
I look into your pretty eyes, there's no logic
for me that can explain why! The possibility of
what we could be, I never ever thought I'd see
the day you would come to me. You triggered a
love deep down in my soul; you gave me your
life for mine, and you made me whole. These
are the reasons why I love you so and the reason
why I will never ever let you go."

Huh, huh, slowly embracing, in real time, the
unexpected exhaling breath of relief from the tortures
of an external frustration conceived in the womb of
a dream molested by her nightmare on Elm Street
Freddy Krueger lover's trickery, Mrs. Destiny lowers
her weapon and turns with what appears to be an
uninterrupted flow of water streaming from a busted
pipe that smears the make-upped canvas of her face.

Thinking, as she proceeded to walk away, about all the hell he brought her to, fueled more by the memories of his degradation towards her and less by his all of a suddenly changed heart, she turns back with a vengeance in the female personification of the Incredible Hulk scorned with the loads of heavy baggage she resents having had to carry. Unbecoming to the charm of his proverbial bars, she presumes he spit from an old verse of rhyme he previously used in a song she heard before, she lifts up the steel piece of her firearm, heated with the flame of her fury resting on the flesh of her mutilated heart, and savagely delivers a one-sided overly dramatic speech to the last known address where the ears of love sarcastically minimized the emotion of her spoken word into the hellish abyss of irrelevance.

"You, you, you hurt me! And now you seek, parenthetically, to excuse your absence with an unauthorized pass, I think you wrote in an attempt to convince me to allow the supposedly reformed you back into the classroom of my love. BOY PLEASE! The passive passivity of your past passed down through the 'pimping ain't easy' irrevocable tragedy of your fatherly pedigree, is the plotted platform that projects the generational wounds of all my pained passions in the presence of my contentious present. You've changed? Huh, really! All of a sudden, the change I have longed for all these years has decided to make an appearance after leaving me with a litany of documented no shows that constantly play in my mind. You haven't changed, but, but I have!"

Then, with an unshakable wrath, masked in the resentment for her part-time lover, she passionately sings, with the anguish of a woman scorned, the culminating verse of every cheated woman's frustrated lyric, no man trying to reclaim the esteemed value of the diamond he lost wants to hear, "I AM Done with Youuuuuuuuuuuuuuuuuu!" The echo of her words pulsating the chambers of his transformed heart leaves him standing numb now having for the first time to embrace the possible reality of having to consider what his life might be without the radiance of her diamond's shine accommodating him on his life journey. "No more!" The thoughts of his mind cry out loudly for the purpose of you the reading audience to comprehend the depth of his dilemma within the soulish realm of his internally contentious posture. No more of her tender kisses, her Janet Jackson "il me plaît d'être avec toi" *Funny How Time Flies* sensually orgasmic fruit cultivating in the secrecy of her garden where he still would like to glean. No more of his destined lover forfeiting herself over to his spontaneous nightly tease, reminding her of love all over, expressed through the romantically seductive sentiments of his inner Aaron Hall.

So just where do they stand, after pontificating with the utmost clarity, the projected rationales of their relentlessly stubborn postures, smothered in the fatigue of all the memorable mistakes they never learned how to forgive and forget? Can she calm down the outspoken posterior of her embarrassed femininity, with a more intense dedication towards restoring her wounded heart through the therapy of Godly relations, while maturing into the fulfilled complexity of a woman capable of loving herself enough to allow the enemy of her lover the right to love her once again?

Underestimating the ability of her supposedly transformed lover's consciousness regarding the underexplored depths of her complications, the effects resulting from the inflicted abuse for which she feels he is the cause, she with the inked blood of all her wounded transgressions files for divorce, in the justifiable holiness of her Jesus freak. Quantifying her decision for divorce on the backbone of that commonly heard cliché, "It is the Lord's Will," most often used in the ignorant bliss constructed by believers and pagans, she leaves the enamored audience engulfed in this couple's tizzy, asking that extremely controversial question, "When, if ever, did Jesus File for Divorce?"

When Jesus Filed for Divorce

Session Eight

"Few people who marry plan for their marriages to fail, but neither do they specifically plan for success."

"There is no limit to what the Lord can do in and with and through any individual or any married couple who surrender themselves and their resources completely to His will and His way."

Dr. Myles Munroe

Sweating, conflicted about whether or not he should open the hand-delivered envelope, he had reluctantly signed for upon delivery to his door, stamped in bold letters with the name and new address of his soon to be ex-wife on it, the Superhero Lover releases a grasping for air sound that abruptly invades the confidence of his atmosphere with a stunned look into the life of his uncertain and unexpected future without the accommodation of Destiny's help. Aware of the content, delicately pressed down and organized accordingly for him to sign after conceding over to the conditions, he ponders around for a few days hoping that his unauthorized subscription of this documented content might magically transform into a reconcilable manuscript that would cause her, out of her concern of its reception, to call and ask, "Did you get my love letter?" Mr. Lover, however, upon a more thorough review of this sensitive document learns that the love that once united his super with the sexy and vivaciousness of his wife's destiny has decided that it no longer chooses to live here anymore. In disbelief, struggling to accept the incomprehensible tragedy of two lovers lost in translation, he with a hereditary stutter caused by his anxiety, painfully, but aggressively, cries out for what seemed like a lifetime before forcing out the nullifying word, "Di, Di, Di, div, div, div, divor, divor, ce, ce, di-vorce! Now faced with the challenge of deciding whether or not he should be left with the burden of pulling the plug on their love, barely surviving on life support, the urgency of Mrs. Destiny's request for him to sign their certificate of death has been confirmed by her and awaits the ink of his John Hancock to proceed with the most traumatizing moment of every failed relationship's catastrophic end—Divorce.

"Is this the end," of love, flat-lined on relationship's bed of death, content without ever using the defibrillator to resuscitate Love's life back into the blood flowing through the once unified vein of two broken hearts? Could it be that all the accolades that attracted Ms. Destiny to the promised strength of the Superhero residing in the package of his Lover was all just a sham, clothed in the mythical fallacy of a fantasy in which he assured her, no guaranteed her, she would be satisfied? Couldn't they possibly figure out a way to be happily ever after, without so easily throwing in the towel on their marriage with the least little fight to make what seemed wrong, right? Now the Superhero disgruntled with the reporting opposition on this topic voices his displeasure with some slight revisions to an interview by former NBA superstar Allen Iverson, about practice, to echo his counter argument openly venting for all the relationship fake news reporters to hear, "Divorce! Divorce! We talkin bout Divorce! We are here at this point talking about divorce? Not Marriage! No, no not Marriage, but Divorce!"

Why and how could she do the Superhero Lover that way and sign off on the purposed divorce decree naively penning her motivation for filing to be because "It Is the Lord's Will!" Really, as strange as it may sound her logic should intrigue couples leaning towards marital dissolution to discover the truth of the answer to this question: So, when, if ever, did Jesus file for divorce?

The dissolution of a forever promised into the shell-shocked abyss of nothingness is the downward spiraling that causes lovers to gesture sarcastically at love apathetically. Today, forever, unfortunately, is set on a timer scheduled to go off in the mind of the irresponsibly immature, handicapped with a softness that easily irritates their flesh when challenged to reach into the hope of tomorrow while faced with the frustrating menacing of today. Forever, in most relationships, no longer stands on the integrity of the word it vowed under oath in the presence of God as it's witness, but on the slippery slopes of rampant emotions that forever's and romantics show apathy towards when breaching the unconditional love requirements needed for the unfolding of a love story on earth that God previously scripted in eternity past. With this nonchalant approach into an openly exploratory sphere of love relations, it is no wonder that the high frequency of the word "Divorce" has for years maintained the top spot on the TMZ most inevitable relationships outcome topic chart.

It is, therefore, safe to concur with the expertise of the late great Dr. Myles Munroe that the truth is "Few people who marry plan for their marriages to fail, but neither do they specifically plan for their success." The knowledge of how to love is a more influential core principle in the good success of love relations, than the idea of love itself. Unfortunately, the ignorance of love unlearned has caused novice lovers to become infatuated with the ecstasy of emotions that covet love's presentation with little to no investment into the mind, will, and emotions of its truth.

The truth is love, when rediscovered in the truth of its natural form, has already, prior to the existences of its finders, set itself on a course for those blessed to travel down its destined road to enjoy acting out the roles love scripted for them to play in its plan. Love when previously planned, without the aid of its pursuers, only requires the surrendering of the will's, of those parties willing to make the sacrificial investment into its wealth over to the mind, will, and emotion of its truth. When two lovers happily surrender their souls over to love's will then and only then will the radiance of love's perfect reflection shine brightly through their relationship. Once again, it is important for me to remind you that the hardest thing for anyone to have to do in this life is to surrender their will, mind, and emotions, over to the greater and perfect will of love. The difficulty of compliance with this required prerequisite for love's manifestation is observed as a door that leads down to the basement of the unknown with a serial killer called pride waiting at the bottom of the steps, energized by the fear of vulnerability. Somehow in our present world, the fear of becoming vulnerable to the conscious minds of those love is unable to control, has caused many to partake in love's formality without exploring its depth that can only be revealed in the presence of two souls unconditionally committed to its truth shared in the maturity of its intimacy.

The inherent nature of love's truth is immutable and uncompromisingly consistent in the conduct of its character regardless of the acceptance or rejection of its possibility of existence in the realm of one's perceived reality. The beauty of love's ability to exist simultaneously in multiple dimensions of reality without ever compromising the integrity of its character is an infectious quality that affirms the truth of its being, even when those wounded by the imposters of its creed seek to rebel against it and consider its possibility to be an illogical rationale impossible to be conceived. The authenticity of love's intentions, like truth, is an existence that can only be perceived through revelation, influenced little by private interpretation. Love is immutably, unchangeably devoted to its pursuer's mastery of its content, outlined in the lessons He, God, preplanned, uninterrupted by the passionate emotions of those that angrily try to resist its temptation. In other words, love does not change. If the participants of its pleasure, however, declare it as good as gone in their relationship because of their changed hearts, then their choice not to love anymore in no way diminishes the value of love's presentation when revealed through a right vessel built to handle the pressure of love's supply given to meet the demand of the audience it was designed for. The wonder of love is that it does not change, but the complexity of love requires for pursuers to conform to its will in order for lovers to reap all the benefits stored up in the fullness of its satisfying pleasures.

So, was this the love that the Superhero Lover and the Sexy and Vivacious Ms. Destiny were feeling when they stepped in the name of love down the red carpet of matrimonial bliss? Is it really the love that the two lovebirds, whose love shined bright like a diamond before purchasing their one-way ticket to ride on the soul of loves train, they both had been looking for?

Like the classy lady she is, Mrs. Lover, who requested shortly after filing for divorce a desire to be addressed by her maiden name, Ms. Destiny, walks into the room with her attorney to begin discussing the proceedings for their divorce. As she walks into the room, accompanied by Keyshia Cole's *"I Remember,"* carrying the wrath of all the pain she was certain her Superhero Lover was responsible for on the outer crest of her dainty posture, Ms. Destiny sits down with the uncertainty of an insecure lover's disgust staring across the table at the Superhero, who stands ready to fight at all cost for the continuity of their journey up the stairway to lovers' heaven. "Shall we begin with the delineations," her attorney asks, as the Superhero Lover stares into her pretty eyes, with no need to come up with a logic to explain why he still believes in all the possibilities of what they could be. Reminded of the fragrant aroma of her scented internal delight, that far surpasses the flawless perfection of her external beauty, he stares at her with the Al B. Sure *"Ooh This Love is So"* seductive intensity echoing for her eyes that I won't let you go! Appearing unfazed by the reaffirmation of his love, Ms. Destiny dressed in a black dress, wearing a pair of black tinted sunglasses to hide her eyes, and a platinum bracelet on her right wrist with the letters "WWJD" lit up with an array of expensive diamonds blinding everyone in the room because of the brightness of their shine, sits motionless as if to suggest that their divorce is an inevitable truism the Superhero is going to have to accept no matter if he wants to or not. Disturbed by the numbness of her callous demeanor towards him, confused about the "Whys" influencing her motivation to throw their love away, he kindly asks her while reaching across the table for her hands, to which she angrily withdraws questioning the sincerity of his attempt, "Why Bae, Why? Why divorce?"

With a low murmuring and a very long hesitation, Ms. Destiny cries out reluctantly, trying hard to convince herself to genuinely believe in the words coming out of her mouth, words that she herself is still unconvinced about. She responds with a cliché that most Christians ignorantly use to consummate their illogical logic:

"Perhaps it was never the Lord's will for the two of us to be together! I made a mistake and, and, and it is God who has given me the ok to divorce you!"

"What? What the Hell?" The Superhero responds, projecting out loudly, "I love you, but that is the dumbest answer I have ever heard in my life! Girl please, you are going to have to come to me with something better than that! So, the Lord told you, and Satan told Eve! Unlike Adam, however, I will not allow you to feed the weakness of my maleness with the forbidden fruit you plucked down from a tree God never intended for either of us to eat from. I am God's man, and you are God's woman, and together, through the Grace of God in Christ Jesus, nothing can stop us because in Him we can go all the way up. You walked in here with your black dress, your dark black shades, and your WHAT WOULD JESUS DO solid gold bracelet on, trying to paint with your countenance a picture of regret to shield yourself from the responsibility of loving me with a sensitive heart afraid to love. You are afraid to love me, because of the continuous struggle you face every day with your insecurities, that have convinced you that you are unqualified to be anybody's wife, let alone mine's. Listen I knew you, and I know you. I knew what I was getting myself into before I married you. I was fully aware of your insecurities as well as my own. I know that you are my blessing and the Scriptures tell me that *the blessing of the Lord makes me rich and adds no sorrow.* That's the reason why I love you so and the reason why I choose to never ever let you go!

Bae, please do not take offense to the words that are about to come out of my mouth, but allow me for a moment to be your teacher, and you my school girl, so that I might carefully instruct you on God's intentions without the distorted perceptions of your inner Eve's delusions. You said that our divorce was the Lord's will. So, when did Jesus get divorced?

As it is defined, divorce is the legal decree used to initiate the process of dissolving or separating the supposedly inseparable union of two uniquely different identities intimately connected through the mystery of a covenant wrapped in the soul of a person called marriage. The unity of diversity, the fusing of two different but consensual personalities into one undistinguishable soul longing to become acquainted again with the likeness of the person they were naturally created to become, is the consummation that inevitably alters divorce's first show-stopping appearance in Genesis, clothed in the blanketed words of *"It is not good for man to be left alone."* The inability of man's (male and female) union, separated by gender to explore the benefits of rediscovering the uniqueness of their diversity with which they were previously acquainted, to reconcile his differences within the inner core of himself, has paved a road for the arrogance of divorce to walk on pridefully. In solidarity, God created His e Pluribus Unum—out of two one—inspiring the many to pursue after the restoration of its appropriated supply of sufficiency only God can provide. In the book of Genesis, Chapter 2, Scripture clearly indicates for us that *"God created human beings in His own image. In the image of God, He created them; male and female He created them"* (Genesis 2:27 NLT). The Scripture, however, never identifies the male or the female's awareness of the other's existence while being confined simultaneously in the likable reflection of God's nature. Adam's discovery of the woman, translated from a rib into a skillfully crafted masterpiece that would satisfy the appetite of his desires, was not the remedy God prescribed to resolve the issue of his aloneness. In every indictment of divorce, the assumption of companionship being the glue that keeps two committed souls together, a remedy they hope will allow them to escape the fear and torment of being alone, is the reason most couples file for divorce on the grounds of irreconcilable differences.

The measure of one's loneliness while residing in the mystery of companionship, as opposed to how one's loneliness might be measured without the luxury of a companion, is incomparable. More people today are ferociously tormented by the unexpected reality of loneliness in marriage and thrust all the energy they have left to make the relationship work, into planning a way to escape being confined to that dark hole in the hellish abyss of their relationship penitentiary. It's a more deplorable thing to be lonely in companionship than to infatuate oneself with the over exaggeration of a natural unfolding of aloneness experienced without it. The misery of being so close together with someone physically but soulishly so far apart as the east is from the west is the tragedy of admiration for the beauty of a skyscraper with no depth to its foundation displaying a lack of fortitude at the base of its structure when the wind blows.

Of what significance is your companion's ship if it is not big enough to accommodate the needed request and Godly desires of you, your lover's one and only passenger peacefully sleeping in the stern of your love boat? A companion ship with only one life jacket and two passengers that can't swim has caused us to react selfishly, at the expense of one another, fixated more on the salvation of ourselves even at the cost of each other's demise. How could we be so close in proximity, but so alone in the unfolding of a love story God previously scripted for us in eternity? Here, but our hearts so far away! Together but not connected! Befriended but lonely, and once cherished but now abandoned! These are some of the proverbial bars of an infection's loneliness experienced in the brokenness of two hearts addicted to consummating the perfection of an imperfectly distorted perception of companionship characterized as a romantic ambiance that epitomizes the pinnacle of relational satisfaction.

Foreshadowing the impact of companionship, the ignorance of its engagers with regard to its intended purpose in context and the contemporary relevance of its nature within the framework of an amalgamation of always and forever changing cultures, Jesus admittedly divorces Himself only from the singularity of a misunderstood idea that suggests worshipping the creation rather than the Creator. God is a Creator whose creation was molded to be a conduit used to expose lovers to the knowledge and nature of love existing in the fullness of its form. Plain and simple, Jesus divorced Himself from the possibility of lovers loving without first encountering Him, the knowledge and nature of love in the fullness of its form.

Relationship frustrations that lead most couples to divorce are the result of an unhealthy fixation on the boisterous winds that blow on the surface of the water, creating tidal waves on the seas of marriages that cause them to sink, rather than fixing their eyes on Jesus who helps them to walk on water while the sea is raging. According to this Biblical story, it is important to remember, as long as Peter fixed his eyes on Jesus, the water had to surrender its will over to God's will to accommodate Peter. When he, however, fixed his eyes on the waves he had to surrender his will over to the will of the water. (See Matthew 14:28-31.)

Even in Genesis, when God declares it is not good for the male man to be alone or left to himself, the words "help meet" provided for him translates the Hebrew words *ezer kenegdo*. *Ezer* means "help" and has the same meaning as the word 'help' in English. In *Kenegdo*, 'meet for him,' the root word, *neged*, means 'opposite,' 'in the presence of,' 'over against,' 'in front of,' 'corresponding to,' or 'aside.' The word *kenegdo actually* means 'opposite as to him' or 'corresponding as to him.' Eve was not the help God intended to meet Adam's aloneness, but rather the opposite corresponding as to him God used to help Adam understand another aspect of His, God's, existence in the multiple realities of Adam's human experience.

God's unprecedented ability to authentically reveal a relational empathy towards Adam within the context of every possible outcome that existed within the framework of the human reality, speaks to the uniqueness of His ability to simultaneously exist in varied dimensions without compromising the integrity of His (God's) character. The ultimate objective that God intended to accomplish through the resourcefulness of Eve was for Adam to rediscover that the same God that promised never to leave nor forsake him is always willing to adjust the satisfaction of His sufficiency to personify Himself in a practical way for humanity to understand, His understanding of each of their inner struggles that come to torment them into their individual shell of isolation. In the realm of male and female companionship, the only relationship God, in the beginning, joined together and declared never to let any man put asunder, was the union of Eve and Adam. God has always sought to reveal the most intimately undisclosed aspects about His nature in and through this relationship encounter.

God commissioned Adam and Eve to be fruitful, by disclosing for each other qualities of His nature they both needed for the two of them to reconstruct the artistic mastery of God's nature, authentically reflecting their

Creator's existence within the consummation of their oneness. Eve was a masterpiece in God's creation. He created her to reflect His nature; Adam needed to see for him to understand how to mature in the confidence of the man longing to be freed from the immaturity of his maleness. Likewise, Adam was for Eve a reflection of some part of God's nature she would only be able to perceive through their experience together, that she needed in order for her to mature in the confidence of the woman longing to be freed from the immaturity of her femininity.

See, lonely people are alone, in their minds, because of a belief triggered by emotionalism that suggests nobody can relate to them without a personal encounter with all the lingering memories and enduring effects of their traumatizing experience. Jesus' desire, however, was never for us to ask for another king, partner, or companion to sit on a throne that was only created for Jesus Himself to occupy. In 1 Samuel 8, Israel asked for a king, without ever reverencing or acknowledging the eternal splendor of the King already occupying the seat on the throne of their hearts. Similar to Israel's desire for a king to be like other nations, people in our world, pursuing after companionship today, fantasize over the imposturous allusion of a plethora of altered images of couples posted on social media sites that project an attitude of escapism through the misguided practice of companion showmanship. Longing for the only true fellowship Jesus can satisfy, they shield all others from the loneliness of their hearts' cry. Jesus says it like this in Luke 12:51-53 (NIV):

"Do not think that I have come to bring peace on earth? No, I have come to divide people against each other. From now on, five in one household will be divided, three against two and two against three. They will be divided, father against son and son against father, mother against daughter and daughter against mother, mother-in-law against daughter-in-law and daughter-in-law against mother-in-law."

Jesus here divorces Himself and His followers from a shallow form of intimacy, inspired through biological chemistry and blended family connectivity created through the marital union, that sought to prioritize the emotions of these relationships above a prerequisite of companionship with Jesus, all couples need to stabilize the branches of their extended relations with Him. When Jesus filed for divorce

His desire was never to break free from a matrimonial covenant He established, but rather for two previously acquainted souls to rediscover through, their union, the highest level of intimacy possible with Jesus, their King, as the only objective needed to be fulfilled whenever seeking to rediscover the purpose of their co-existence. No marriage with two diabolically opposed personalities frustrated by a plethora of unsatisfied fantasies created through an unhealthy appetite of ill-advised fixations, wishing for the pleasure of companionship from outsiders over the satisfaction of a desired companionship, first, with the Greater One in us, will ever be everything it is supposed to be without Jesus.

Bae, God's desire was never for us just to be better at marriage, but rather to always be our best reflection of those aspects of His nature He created for us to be for each other in our marriage. He intended for us, through our companionship, to paint a picture of Him that would bear evidence of our Creator's existence in the individual oneness of our spiritually consummated show of companionship. You and I are not standing here at the altar of divorce, ready to give up on us, because this is the Lord's will, but rather because of our ignorance in demanding for one another to relieve each other from a fear of a loneliness that nullifies the priority of Jesus as the most suitable companion we both needed to encounter individually, before coming on-board this companion ship that you now have concluded you no longer want to ride.

So, what's it going to be Bae? Are you willing to leave your better foot behind, and put your best foot forward for the sake of our marriage? Divorce is not an option for me. I am committed 'til death do us part. So, what's it going to be, Bae? Do you still love me, or do you choose to love me no more? Can you learn how to love me again even though you don't like me?"

How to Love a Love You Don't Like

Session Nine

"Your Life Experiences are only small events that occur in a much Larger Reality."

Shaun S. Saunders

The illogical reality of two lovers specifically created to co-exist in a frame of time predetermined by God to reflect love in the purest expression of its original form is the hope inevitability every couple initially aspires to capture in the commonly misinterpreted timed realm of a love called Destiny. "We were destined to be together" the echoing sentiments of novice lovers, fixated on the fantasies of love without ever acknowledging the frustration of its sweat and the bloody tears collected from the continuity of its sacrifice. The assumptions that destiny, God's merging of people or things together to fulfill His purpose with an attitude rooted in the promising reward of interdependence, is God's formatted blueprint that automatically leads to relationship success, even without the uncompromising services of its headliners, is a fallacy. Just because God destined two individuals to always and forever be, the possibility of the two of them ever meeting destiny depends largely in part on the continued daily contributions of their devotions towards God first and their unwavering commitment towards one another. In no way should lovers ever assume just because they were destined by God to be together that the ignorance of their response to destiny's call, when it calls, might still inevitably guarantee them success in their relations, because of their association with Destiny's name.

As the Superhero Lover awaits Mrs. Destiny's response to the question "Can you ever find it in your heart to love again what you don't like," The Daily Times most diabolical reporter, The Accuser, abruptly stands up during the divorce proceeding and sarcastically shouts out, "How in the hell is she supposed to do that?" Turning and speaking to Mrs. Destiny, with absolutely no regard for her Superhero Lover's presence, the Accuser continuing with his awkwardly delusional discourse, publicly propositions her with, "Baby if you divorce this sorry excuse of a man, then I promise you,

you will definitely like the way I, a real Nigg…. I mean man, loves you!" "Does he not see me standing here," the Superhero Lover thinks to himself, taken back by the ruthlessly bold tenacity of The Accuser's well-timed precision and the awesomely calculated execution of his venomously poisonous fangs, injected into the veins of Mrs. Destiny's heart's trust, determined to kill the credibility of any and every rebuttal that could possibly be given to reconcile The Superhero and Mrs. Destiny's love relations.

Drawing closer to his unworthy opponent, who's set out on hindering the momentum of the Superhero and Mrs. Destiny's love thang from moving forward, the Superhero and the accuser have a stare down, facing one another like two gunslingers ready to shoot it out for the hand of a woman uncomfortable with committing her heart to loving or liking either one of them. As they stand face to face with their hands gently caressing their sidearm ready to shoot to the death with the bullets of their words, both determined to make a case for why they are the best out of the better of the two of them, Mrs. Destiny intercedes between the ignorance of their competitive quarreling over their presumed rights to her heart responding to the Superhero's question with the following words: "The Accuser is right. How can I love you again, my lover, if I don't like you?"

Now with his eyes fixed on what appears at first glance to be a two-on-one gun slinger's advantage working against him, with it appearing that Mrs. Destiny is ready to do a sign and trade of her rights from the Superhero Lover team over to team Accuser of the Brethren, the Superhero Lover is still poised to fight, wondering if what he is fighting is still worth fighting for. He reluctantly listens to hear the details of her benediction to which he is scared he will find himself locked outside the once open window through which she believes all of her blessings will be poured out. As the Accuser prematurely stagger struts down the winner's Relationship Hall of Fame, with the snickering laugh of a smooth-talking pimp going to collect some of his change from one of his tricks, he is greeted by the absence of the treasured trophy whose body he was naively convinced he had won over, as Mrs. Destiny swiftly maneuvers her way from him, in a rude and curt manner, and turns towards the Superhero Lover, angrily demanding that he answer her question. "Answer Me" the echoing repetitions of these words repeated with an extreme fierceness and intensity that reveals the aggression with which she is pursuing after an answer to this question that continues to stalk her through the ignorance of its silence. This is the only lifeline the Superhero Lover may have left to convince Mrs. Destiny to change her mind. "Answer Me! What, the cat got your tongue? Oh, so now you don't have anything to say? Answer Me RIGHT NOW," the pitied fool of her traumatized heart cries out with an intimidating stare expressing her frustration with his tendency to answer questions she never asked him to avoid any responsibility in addressing the issues standing toe-to-toe with her, challenging her face-to-face.

His silence is not merely a loss for words, but a therapeutic collision positioning Mrs. Destiny at this moment in time to speak her mind and her concerns, for her to hear, through the echoing sound of her thoughts spoken in her own words. This allows this supposedly mistreated wounded damsel to discover that the answer to the question she has been waiting so long for, lies in the problem she has been warring with within herself. With the Superhero Lover trying to figure out how to play his hand with the cards he's been dealt, Mrs. Destiny moves to counter his bluff with these words openly venting the extremes of her agony, while subliminally confronting the true perpetrator of her problem, herself.

"Your deafening silence speaks when it comes to you answering my question, with an impotence that reveals a lack of concern for meeting the needed thing I am demanding from you. I remember you once told me that your love is contagious. Then does your silence imply that I've been cured from the infection of your love that convinced my heart to slow dance with the promises of its expression in the silence of a word, once but no longer displayed through the power of your actions? Your presence used to trigger a love deep down within my soul, flustering my head with your inspirational Love sayings like, "Woman, God possessed me with the resourcefulness, power, strength, attitude, will, and integrity to love you the way He always knew you needed to be loved." I can in no way deny that in my heart I still chose to love you, but the emotions with which I tend to express this love is magnified with a dislike for the flawed armor of the person God has chosen for His love to flow through to get to me. You always told me that wisdom is the ability to see a person in whatever capacity God created them to exist, and not to expect them to be anything more or less than the person God naturally created them to be. So even when the person you love doesn't look anything like the person you think God created them to be for you, it is still your responsibility as the recipient lover to see and say about them what God saw and said about them. When you, however, are not feeling somebody the way, you once felt them before, this kind of counsel comes across as a more problematic resolve that seems to be an impossible reality unlikely, at least in my estimation, to be obtained. The fluency of my desire for love's promise that used to send chills up and down the indestructible force of my inner lover's backbone has paralyzed the act of my will, leaving me numb and void of the tinkling sensation I thought love was supposed to make me feel.

Is love not supposed to feel good, or right? From the time I was a little girl I waited and longed for love to knock on my door. I played over and over in my head the happily ever after ending of my love story. My story was a fantasy, absent the luxury of a normal love story's traditional features such as conflict, or the mischievous antics caused by evil forces from the dark side, eager to disrupt the unity of two unstoppable lovers. I liked it because it made the little girl in me hide in the safety of my father's security while waiting with an eager expectation for the man in my dream to seek out and find my hiding place. It was like all the movies I saw, the books I read, and all the great stories I heard from my elders who always seemed to be clothed with a look of love that most certainly epitomized the inevitability of lovers' success. But then I met you, the reality of my fantasy that caused me to rethink the myth of my childhood allusion with love. After waiting all my life for you to come, you by the grace of God defied the odds of all the tragedies mounted up against you in your own life just to find me, the rib you had been longing for that would cause both of us to wake up to love. You, you, you were all the man I needed and more. In our ignorance, we quickly moved to loving and liking one another as lovers, without ever learning how to love and like one another as friends, first.

Our jubilant optimism, blinded by the expectancy of love's caress, caused us to ignorantly glamourize the urgency of our lust for one another in the darkened light of love's distorted reflection. We messed up! We prioritized the lust of our flesh and the lust of our eyes above God's most authentic expression of love in the pure essence of its person. We established the credibility of our relationship on the weakness of our emotions, and then sought God, in the strength of His power, to regenerate a collapsing structure that was never sure about the strength of its foundation. If we had matured in our relations with God first before ever coming together, and then have become reacquainted with one another second, the foundation of our union together would have been sure from the beginning because it would have been built on the certainty of Jesus as our rock. We, however, learned love out of the egregious cravings of our lust that convinced our hearts that love was an emotion that needed to be managed by our emotions. But through trial and error, we learned that love is not an emotion, but a person.

Love is a person, not an emotion. Love is the Person of God in Christ revealing the deep depths of His devotedness towards, you and me, the primary objectives He created to draw out an authentic expression of His conduct and character. It is unfortunate but love, when misunderstood, for us, obscured our vision and deceived our eyes. This whole time I never knew that I was longing for the nature of God's love I needed in you to love all of me, including my imperfections through the imperfection of your fragile frame. In you, I looked for God's perfect love that cast out all fear, but my misunderstanding of love choked my expectation and caused me to be afraid with the tormenting shame of exposing the nakedness of my vulnerability in the presence of His person. I'm scared of loving you! I've tried, but it seems like no matter what I try to do, fear hinders me from giving you the best of my love. I have never given you the best of my love because to do it; I had to change my mind and surrender my will over to the greater will of God. This still is the hardest choice I am struggling to make work and attempting to fulfill in my life. I finally understand, now, that God loves me so much that He willingly placed the perfection of Himself inside of the imperfection of you, to penetrate the walls of my imperfections just so He could touch the quiver of my soul with the suffocating embrace of His love.

When we first set out on our journey to rediscover love's desired outcome for us, the wandering of our lusty eyes downloaded onto the hard drive of our mind, will, and emotions a virus that masked our knowledge of how to authenticate love's existence within the oneness of the person our union destined we would become. You were my falling feeling that shackled me into the arms of a lover that chose me without any consultation with the intentions of my will, set out to inspire me to love with my eyes closed. I discovered, however, that love is not a falling feeling, but a daily decision to practically reveal the possessed power of Christ, working through me, that He intended for me to extended towards the lover He designated for me to care for.

Upon our first experience with love, we ignorantly assumed that it fell on us like a provocative lap dance delivered by a stripper lustfully luring the cravings of a patron's heart with the illusion of a dishonest seduction that paralyzes its victims, ultimately confining them to her will without their choosing. Like every misguided patron that comes to make it rain, believing that his actions are the result of a stripper's perfected nakedness that caused him to fall under the gyrating spell of a stripper's hypnosis, falling in love is the most unreasonable excuse lovers give to dismiss themselves from the responsibility of their choice to love because they chose to, rather than because love chose them without their permission. Out of the blessed independence of our human wills, we both, decided to love each other with the confident assurance, at least at the time, that we were possessed with and the sovereignty of God's power to supply the demand for one another's need to be loved. Although I believe I am possessed with the power to love you the way God knew you needed to be loved, the will with which I should now choose to do that conflicts with my desire to fulfill the conjugal privileges of the due benevolence, I vowed to always and forever shower you with.

Why? is the question I have continued to ask myself, over and over again, stuck in the numbness of an ignorance that offers me no relief from an emotional bipolar disorder. Could it be because of you, or could it be because of me placing the delicacy of our loving hearts in the blender of destruction smoothing down our love like two softies rather than preserving it like a well-tenderized steak? Could it be because you elected to announce publicly, with little consideration of how your venting might have influenced my sanity regarding our relationship, the luxury of your option to choose to LOVE ME OR TO LOVE ME NO MORE? How can you be my King, if, at the point of aggressive resistances, you fold your strength under the pressure of my calamity and have the audacity even to think you have an option to rescue me or let me drown in the undercurrent of angry waters attempting to swallow up my soul? You are the lifeguard I trusted to remind me that I was safe from the possibility of ever drowning again in the boisterous waves of my relationship disappointments. Sometime after we married, however, the undercurrent of your wandering eyes pulled down my confidence below the surface of love's promises, drowning me in the shallow waters of its uncertainty. Upon discovery of my lifeless body, pulled from the wallowing pity of my disgrace, you left me floating in the sea of my sadness without ever moving toward me to revive me back to life. How could you bare to leave me, my King, companion, my friend, struggling to survive the guilt that overwhelmed me like a burden too heavy to bear, without breathing the breath of your life into the lungs of the loving soul you vowed to protect?

Listen! Listen! For far too long you have ignored the sound of my heart's cry because of your mind's inability to transition its perspective, once greeted with the external expressions of my internal dilemmas. Your passivity and unaggressive resolve towards helping me have allowed me to justify in my mind an unattractive disdain for the presentation of your person that has challenged me with the difficulty of continuing to love a lover I dislike. Could it solely be all because of you, that I find myself passing the blame, like Adam, on God *declaring "the man you put me here with, gave me some fruit from the tree and I ate it"*? How could it possibly be because of anything or anybody else, but you? It's not me, because I have done nothing, absolutely nothing wrong throughout the duration of our relationship. There is no way, no way the cracks in our relationship foundation are the result of all the loving sacrifices I have made for you. I can't accept that. Me! It can't be because of me! No, it had to be because of you, not me, doesn't it?

I have tried to stop loving you, but I can't seem to escape the thrill of love's intoxicating sensation. Why can't I get my body to ignore what my mind says and just walk away from you? I tried to keep myself on track to walk away, but I keep stumbling back into this bed spread with the need to be loved in a way only God possessed you with a continuous supply to provide. I was always told that I was supposed to find love, so I went hunting to discover its whereabouts. In today's world, they tell young lovers to "live your truth." In other words, if you don't find it, make up in your mind an idea of whatever you want it to be to fit into your understanding of what you have determined your life was supposed to become. Amazingly, just now I realized and have come to discover that love was never lost, so it never needed to be found. But love, this entire time, has relentlessly sought out my location to find me. I was wrong! I thought it was solely because of your passivity that you were a "Man Down," emasculated by the tormenting devils shackling you in the prison of your insecurities. It was me holding you down with the restraints of my fear of love, the chokehold of my own insecurities dangling around your neck, and the unrealistic pressure of my demands resting like a burdensome weight on your shoulders too heavy for you to carry.

Traditionally, it has been said that a wife is supposed to allow her husband to be the man in the relationship. The word "allow" here means "to permit to occur." Throughout the course of my relational interactions with the opposite sex, I found this irrational comment to be the ignorance of my truth, which I chose to believe in the reality of my relationships. As a result, every male I presumed it was my duty to allow to be a man, left me except for you. As your wife, "allowing" you to be the man echoes the sorrowful pity of an angry mother still breastfeeding her spiritually, intellectually, and physically capable adult male child. I should have known you never needed me to allow you to be the man because this comment itself undermines the natural order and purpose of your existence with those unattainable measures that redefine manhood from the perspective of my female demand, instead of God's plan. Allowing you to be the man in our relationship leaves it up to you to figure out, alone, what is in the best interest of us, with little accountability regarding decisions made in the isolation of your discretion. The implication of allowing you to be the man invalidates the man your male needed me as a wife to help you become, by permitting me to dismiss myself as God's ultimate challenger, created with the influential authority to place a demand on you to evolve from the breastfeeding adolescence of your maleness, into the matured responsible man God expects you to be.

My job was not for me to use the privileges of my submission as an excuse to remove myself from the role of a helper towards the man God created me to defend, but rather to challenge God's strong man, confined to the walled insecurities of your male imperfections, to rise up and lead your family from the postured dominion of your God-given authority.

My misunderstanding of this principle caused me to illegally challenge you to a fight with the ruthlessly nonchalant attitude of my uncompromisingly big-headed ego! I presented myself to you as your wife dressed in the cloth of submission without ever sincerely associating myself with the power of its purpose that would allow me to love on you the right way in the secrecy of those areas where you appear to be most vulnerable. I neglected the duties of my services after listening to the severity of your request because I thought the despondency of your chase after my heart became shallow in depth in comparison to my chase after you. If I would have known during the early stages of love's ecstasy to focus my aim on chasing after God rather than chasing after a man, then God would have had the right man chasing after me. Insecure in the obscurity of my first thoughts about you, I questioned if you were the right man God intended to chase after and maintain all the needed repairs on my well-oiled machine. You were supposed to be my driver, possessed with the power of God to maneuver my doubting heart from the demise of my past into the loving arms of the future God destined for us together. Yes, driving Mrs. Destiny was the motto I used to evaluate the pleasure principle of my time in your presence to determine if the driving distance of my infatuation with you on this ride along would reveal my compatibility with a man I kept choosing to love. The question, then, we both are searching to rediscover the answer to is not centered around how to love a lover you don't like, but rather how to like again a lover whose dedicated heart continues to reject your attempts at choosing not to love no more.

Our current dilemma has little to do with love, but more to do with learning how to like again what the choices of our choosing continue to compel us to love more and more. I don't like you, at times, but I still choose to love you forever. This psychological quandary disrupting the consistency of our thought lives has created a dysfunctional pattern of double-mindedness that has caused us to be unstable in all our marital ways. Your choosing whether to love me or love me no more or my trying to figure out how to love again a lover I don't like, echoes the burdensome load of our unhealed self-inflicted wounds that we have determined, without cause, to shift the blame of an assault we committed on ourselves onto the innocence of one another's unconditioned love. For most of our love, we have blamed each other and accepted the blame, out of the innocence of our desire to be each other's problem solver for certain tragedies in our relationship that we should have never blamed each other for. With the ruthlessly relentless waves of success always expected to accompany love's picturesque masterpiece shattered by the broken pieces of both our sinking hearts, we selfishly depended on one another's rescue party to relieve us from the struggle of the raging seas we both discovered we were drowning in.

Seeing more clearly now, I have come to understand, through my progressions learned while carelessly wondering down the street of trial and error, that the aggression of my dislike for you was strikingly comparable to the diminishing value of the likability I had for myself. "If I diminish you, then I diminish myself" (Bishop Desmond Tutu). I see now my dislike for you had nothing to do with the passive energy you showed during your attempts at rescuing me, but more to do with my distaste with you not fulfilling your designated role in a way that I selfishly revised for you to play in a love story I did not write. All this time it was because of me. The bitterness of my entitled heart, whose desire I acknowledged first, directed me to revise the lines of your script, changing your role to justify the rationale for my inability to conform my mind, will, and emotion to the identity of the character God casted for me to play in the love story He authored, for us. My infatuating obsession with "the Perfect Man" basking in the fullness of love's expression in the completed packaging of its person caused me to mistakenly love you in the beauty of my created perfection without taming the emotional roller coaster ride of my likes and dislikes I tucked away like landmines in the field God required for you to navigate the adolescence of your maleness to become a good man. I dated you as the man I imagined in the beauty of my created perfection, hoping your perfect presence would overshadow the imperfect love I showered in, to scrub the dirty stench off my filthy conscience. Because of a declining confidence of my perception of myself, I decided during our courtship to introduce you to the glorious glow of my protective shield, the only defense I could think of to secure, with my own hands the salvageable pieces of my heart, after encountering the previous traffic jams of love's disappointment that stole away the irreplaceable parts of my soul. My soul is wounded, trafficked by countless unaffectionate lovers, who spilled seeds of empty words in the unprepared soil of my fertile garden, leaving me pregnant with self-hatred that caused me to neglect laboring in my own vineyard.

By preoccupying myself more with laboring in the fertility of your field, gathering harvested fruits that would bring the utmost pleasure to you, I missed out on tending to my own and have been lost in the dark for some time now, on which direction to go to rediscover its previous location. The lost land I am referring to is the perfected image of God, expressing the perfection of Himself through the imperfection of a phenomenal woman called, ME! This woman, to which I can't recall ever meeting, is the fertile field with a plenteous harvest waiting for the right one to pluck up the fruit the Lord of the harvest prepared specifically for the laborer He sent to work it. Part of the problem with us is largely due to my continued unwillingness to indulge in how to man my own field responsibly. How can I or you, as my lover, plant seeds of affirmation into the rich soil of a fertile womb to which I, the owner of the land has yet to explore the quality of its worth for myself carefully?

See, all my life I had to fight, intimidated by the thought of walking beside the success of God's woman quieted within me.

So honestly my dislike for you, my love, is not rooted in the acrimonious clutches of an adulterous affair, or any known abusive sabotaging of actions caused by you that made me bitter. It is, however, because of the powering presence of God's love personified through the imperfection of your person ruthlessly challenging me to take my turn walking in the shoes of the phenomenal woman my insecurities convinced me I could never be. My fear now is greater because of my mind's inability to mold myself into the scripted idea of your demanding aspiration, requesting for me to model the character of a woman whose footsteps I am unable to trace. She is the lady you desire to come running towards the heavily guarded throne of your heart at the lowering of your scepter bidding her to approach you her King in the honorable glory of your heavenly queen. Though I consider it a privilege for you having awarded me the legal right to sit beside you throughout your reign on our throne, I am not sure at this time if I can verify that the identity of the woman sitting beside you in that chair is really me.

The answer to this question is that I don't know. My unfamiliarity with the queen character and the posture of her existence in the reality of my story is unknown.

Only to you, my Superhero Lover, have I confessed all these things to explain for you in detail the motivation behind my decision to divorce a lover I love but don't like. I don't like you because I've never learned how to like all of me. It is for this reason that I have concluded that it would be in the best interest for me to separate myself from us and devote my attention towards capturing the presence of the Godly woman that has always anonymously invaded the immaturity of my female mind with a perfectly pictured photo of our love with her as your headliner. She is not just some random chick or the object of a fantasy you have always unfairly desired, but she is the perfect woman you see in me when observing me through the eyes of God. If we will ever be happy again together—loving and liking one another—it is imperative that I secure the damaged soul of my little girl, waiting in the security of her God image, eager to escape through the packaging of the woman sitting beside you on the throne of our relationship. I am not certain, yet, where

I stand with you, due largely in part to my uncertainty on where I stand within the reality of becoming one with myself. Honestly, how long can I hold up the lie of my perfect picture pose before collapsing under the flashing lights of the malicious paparazzi seeking to point out the flaws of our picture-perfect photo that we ignorantly convinced ourselves was flawless? Where do we go from here? I am not sure, but do you believe without this time apart, we can continue to camouflage our dislikes with love in the framing of a perfect picture that's not picture perfect? Do you?"

Picture Perfect

Session Ten

"The difference between a perfect picture and a picture perfect is simple. A perfect picture reflects images of love, to an audience of many, to give the deceitful impression of an unspeakable joy shared between two distant lovers. A picture perfect, however, authentically reflects the glorified excellence of challenged lovers, who continue to fight with love, capturing a glimpse in real time of loves reward, working through them, on the other side of love's journey called victory."

Shaun S. Saunders

The striking distance between love revelations, as they are perceived through the photographic memory of love's mind, and its continuing conflict with the unmerited desires of the human will absent the revelation of God and His Word has blurred the beauty of all of God's original photos that use to reflect the epitome of love in the image of its person. Now lovers work harder, instead of smarter, to recapture an idea of love they hoped would remind them of a picture-perfect picture God previously captured, on His camera, downloaded with the forgotten memories of love's splendid display always known to accompany the presence of an existence once highly demanded. Unlike the fuzzy obscurity of a photo shot through the unreliable lens of a photographer, who deceitfully hinges the integrity of his pictures on a false narrative that hides away the imperfections of his relational infrastructure with his most respected client by embellishing on the extremities of his work, God's picture-perfect photo authentically reveals love holistically exemplifying the perfection of God working through the imperfection of two lovers perfect for each other.

The difference between a perfect picture and a picture perfect is simple. A perfect picture reflects images of love, to an audience of many, giving a deceitful impression of an unspeakable joy shared between two distant lovers with egos never messaged by love's rough hands. A picture-perfect picture, however, authentically reflects the glorified excellence of challenged lovers, who continue to fight with love, capturing a glimpse in real time of love's reward, working through them, on the other side of love's journey called victory. The truth is that the perfection of a picture is not found in the posturing pose of the images highlighting its canvas but in the origin of a reflection that authentically reveals the complexity of all the independent parts unified in the oneness of its presentation. Perfect pictures have been known to falsify reflective expressions, usually posted on social media sites such as Snapchat, Facebook, Instagram, and Twitter, undermining the implementation of a supposedly believed idea with the absent reflection of its natures continued existence long after the picture was taken.

In today's world, lovers have become so addicted to a drug called "likes," a dangerous narcotic sold worldwide by social media drug pushers that cause individuals to uncontrollably convey irrational images of loving excellence without committing themselves to the responses required for them to participate in the stability of love's perfect will. In other words, looking like Gold without the strength and power that enables lovers to bear up under the weight of Gold's load comfortably, is an indication of our infatuation with love's look rather than with the knowledge needed to mature in the perfection of its performance. Yes, lovers indulgently delight in the law of love's appearance, but how to perform up to the demands of its unconditional creed is not an ideal that can be naturally embodied without the bodied work of Christ possessing them, individually, with His mind empowering their person, willfully extending love towards the objectives He's designated.

Now that the results of Mr. and Mrs. Lover's picture-perfect lie detector test finally arriving at what seemingly appears might be the end of their journey together, they both out of respect for one another isolate themselves from the noise of the others around them to make sure their choosing to love or love each other no more is solely based on their decision, uninfluenced by the opinions of outsiders. Now with a better understanding of how the sincere expressions of the affections, they vowed to one another, could never fuse the beauty of their souls together without the crazy glue of God's inseparable love jammed between them, they sit down in the presence of the Wonderful Counselor for a detailed explanation and interpretation of His truth on the revealing results regarding the integrity of their perfect picture's picture-perfect reflection. When it comes to the honesty of the perfect picture reflection you have so flawlessly framed and mounted upon the decorated wall of your troubled marriage, Mr. and Mrs. Lover, the test results from the lie detector test reveal that you are not.....................

Unfortunately, due to the high volume of expected viewers, busy scrolling down the timeline of everybody else's relationship, because of a lack of dedication to the success of their own, tuning in to see what the end of the Mr. and Mrs. Lover saga is going to be, the sound fades out and the camera goes black leaving a nosey audience confused about the reflection of the couples supposedly perfect picture. To avoid the guaranteed possibility of a Reality TV debacle, the Wonderful Counselor puts a stop to the hosting network's determination towards broadcasting the results on all live media streams, to preserve the worthiness of their leftovers from the inevitable repercussions that always follow when airing out dirty laundry. Considering it to be in the best interest of the Lovers to protect their privacy, their Wonderful Counselor escorts them, with a heavy arsenal led presidential like detail, to an undisclosed location to reveal the truths of His findings with them in private.

Upon their arrival to the top-secret location, they are greeted with a ton of required security formalities, they must go through, like everyone else privileged to enter in before being granted access into an atmosphere absent the ridicule of discrimination and the ignorance of prejudice. As the Lovers move through each security point, curious to know if the heavily armed guards examining the hidden parts of their person can detect the shame of their nakedness, they feel a breeze of overwhelming confidence that comforts them as they walk in the perfect shadow of their imperfection. For the first time in a long time, the Lovers felt a sense of safety and security, individually, that allows them to clearly see without any doubt or reluctance of acceptance the diversity of those truths that motivated both their hearts to love. Once they get to the top-secret location, they sit down, waiting for the Wonderful Counselor who promised to meet them in His office upon their arrival. In the presence of a love power that causes an unfamiliar attraction to burn in their hearts, like an addict going through withdrawal, these lovers become infatuated once again with an intoxicating shot of lover's mojo they never allowed each other the favorable privilege of experiencing before. This unfamiliar attraction not rooted in the ecstasy of a lover's seduction, but a deeper level of intimacy shared between the souls of two lovers without the pleasure of any sexual encounter, intoxicated them with a spiritual drink that took them up on a love high they really were not sure they could come down from. Then He enters, the Wonderful Counselor, with the envelope holding the results from the lie detector test in His hands, deflating all the air out of their lover's high balloon with the thought of coming face to face with the distortions of truth deeply stained in the texture of their supposed picture-perfect picture.

"Now that it appears we have managed to successfully isolate the two of you in a safe place outside of the reaches of our unforgiving society's swaying powers, let us officially begin with My commentary on the truths I discovered after reviewing your results. Let Me, first, make it clear that My findings have in no way been altered by the influence of My prejudice or My opinions about either of you or by any irrational criteria from antagonistic outsiders maliciously predicting the outcome of your love story's end. These findings I am about to share with you are based solely on the noticeable flaws deeply stained within the presentation of your self-reflected ideas of perfection. It is, therefore, necessary for me, as your counselor, to bid both of you warning to keep your hearts open to receive the honesty of this truth, embracing your rebellion that contributed to its pain that could quite possibly lead to another martial relationship fatality. Do not under any circumstances attempt to model the hope of success for your relationship after the admirable candor of other lovers' successes because of their willingness to abide by the standards of a love curriculum specifically designed to accommodate their learning styles. There is no one model of excellence epitomizing marital perfection sitting on the throne residing as an absolute power on the pinnacle of God's stairway to heaven. With that said please, please remember to only use the blueprint

God specifically designed to build the quality of your house to ensure that the layout works in the best interest of the two of you.

My objective is to provide you with a spiritual analysis of the flawed and exquisite pieces cohabitating together on the canvas of your desires to infer, based on my professional observation, the means by which you both are convinced have led you up to this point of an unknown end. The test itself highlighted three specific areas of concentration needed to measure the transparency of the makeup used for your photo-optical display against the integrity of the makeupless faces living in the shoes of the picture-perfect characters living behind the bright lights of the camera. These three areas of concentration used to expose the transparency and authenticity of your picture are centered around the natural reflection of the pictures' lighting, the angling prerogative of the photographer responsible for creating its illusion and the quality of the lenses used to verify the truths shared between the images projected through its view and the convicted life these images walk in as perceived through the singularity of its eye.

There is only one truth concerning this or any other matter. The truth you both are about to hear must not be analyzed with the loosely-tied strings that helplessly dangle in the ignorance of your private interpretations rooted in the lying truths you made up in the foolishness of your autonomy. The truth, however, you will discover is revealed through the eyes of My unadulterated wisdom, uninfluenced by the illegitimate truths you used to rationalize your error in the choices of your free will. This test has a less than zero percent probability of being wrong and has proven to hold the only consistent one hundred percent all-time accuracy rating used to successfully rediscover the authentic truth hidden under a laundry load of lies accumulated with the purpose of preserving falsehoods. With all My preliminary conversation out of the way and my gut feeling telling me, "YOU CAN'T HANDLE THE TRUTH," it is with the utmost care and caution that I now present to you the truth about God's picture-perfect presence existing in your perfect picture.

The first area of concentration, the natural reflection of your picture's lighting, used to measure the strength of a connection between the light shining through the produced image and the light of God's presence shining in the life of your relationship, relayed a weak signal of exchange when examined under the light of transparency. Your picture, when placed in front of the light, the mirror used to discern its honest with the agreement of its reflection, only partially reflected an accurate image of the perfect picture, you dressed up as and put on in front of the camera. It appears that the glowing light that supersized the intensity of your well passioned desire for one another, during the ecstasy of your relations, somewhere along the lines of your union begin compromising the power of its unbelievable display of fireworks for the endless frustration of a dark side that blew out the matches needed to keep your lovers fire lit. The image you have projected, therefore, is the counterfeit of a perfect bill, camouflaged in the immeasurable value of perfections pictured garments without the seal of God's approval impressed upon the souls of two lovers once totally committed to performing up to the expectation of His desires. Your picture, though not completely dark, is extremely obscured with dark spots that undermine a radiance that covers lovers with the illuminating light of their inherited ability to perform naturally on the stage of love's delight.

At the core of your relationship, you ignored God's command for you to delight yourself in Him, and have convinced yourselves, without knowledge, to ruthlessly pursue after desired things, that God never desired for you to have. The Scripture in Psalm 37:4, *"If you delight yourself in God, He will grant you the desires of your heart,"* means God will grant you your desire easily because of your maturity in desiring for yourself the things that God has always desired for you to have from the time of your conception. Your lacking delight in providing the highest level of intimacy with God has caused the glaring light explosion of those fireworks that used to capture the attention of your soul to sabotage the innocence of your desires for one another. I have heard the question asked, "How do I love again, a lover that I do not like?" God's love is how lovers mature in the beauty of His perfection. This understanding, however, is unlikely to be attained without ever delighting in the thoughts of love's desire towards you, unhindered by an undisciplined appetite that believes it is entitled to have whatever it wants when it wants it. Your love for one another is imperfect because it is not anchored in the delight of God. If you don't know how to delight yourself in liking the God that you claim to love, it is impossible for you to delight in the sufficiency of God's love packaged in the personality of your destined lover.

The next area of concentration I will discuss with you is the angling prerogative of the photographer responsible for creating your picturesque illusion. I considered the angling perspective of your pictures to be somewhat strange. Was it under the influences of your own discretion or that of the photographer that you opted to take the perfect pictures that you elected to shoot from angles that made you look like acquaintances with benefits rather than lovers with purpose?

The perspective angling from which you have previously chosen to address the undisclosed challenges, issues, and difficulties of your lover's experience contradicts the convictions with which you both guaranteed would be your response to what you believed God determined your relationship would become.

It is extremely important for you to understand that your belief and your conviction are not the same thing. Believing in your companion speaks to your companion's responsibility to you as the objective of their delight and of their investment of time into confirming for you the truths they have chosen to reveal about his or her self. Your belief speaks to the extents and degrees of their devotion to convincing you of their power to perform above and beyond the expectation of the desires you demanded they meet with a working supply. Conviction, on the other hand of these two extremes, is contingent upon you and your response to the truths about your companion they have chosen to reveal. Your conviction holds you accountable, not to convincing them of your truth, but by the nature of a performance known always to accompany your belief that takes pleasure in catering to the satisfaction of what your companion desires from you. These extremes—belief and conviction—are the angling perspectives great photographers always shoot for during their photo shoots. They hope to capture the fusing together of two independent personalities into the newly formed model of an inseparable compound.

Unfortunately, it appears your picture is framed in the arrogance of your autonomy, absent the witness of your companion's testimony needed for the fulfillment of God's presence to authenticate your pictured perfection. Your belief in your companion's ability to convince you they are possessed with a supernatural ability to perform up to the expectations of God's desire for you is blocked with the wavering of your conviction that actively converses with an enemy called despondency. See, your angles reveal the strengths and weakness with the line of sight you have been trained to view; i.e., the relational value of your significant other's contribution obscured by the selfish prerogatives of your own wavering convictions. Your conviction, the tangible evidence that was supposed to escape from your mind and provocatively strut itself down the red-carpeted reality of your anchored beliefs, has failed to show up for its show-stopping performance time after time. As a result of consecutive no-shows to events where your presence was in high demand, the once overly extended invitation to be there for one another in times of need is on the brink of signing off on death's certificate due to the absences of love's pulse.

Simply said, your perfect picture, though not fraudulent, is still not yet picture perfect, because of the lack of unity between the two angling perspectives you have pridefully viewed your loving relationship through. You both need to let go of your pride. As a couple, you have unsuccessfully tried to clothe your relationship with the beauty of love's perfection, with unhealed hearts sinking in the depression of pride caused by imagined and warranted offenses. Your attempts at maintaining your composure after almost drowning in the sea of an offender's offenses has caused both of you to indirectly massage the energy of your rage onto the shoulders of your lover's alibi that exonerates them from being the cause of almost all your offenses.

Your picture is dressed in the modesty of perfection's discipline but bleeds the cold air of death's sting that desires to drain a swamp where you, without any checks or balances, have been freely comforted with asserting the dominance of your own will. Remember, God's love is unconditional, and "unconditional love always gives others the right to hurt us" (John Bevere). Your love for one another, unfortunately, has waxed cold. Matthew 24:12-13 (NIV) says, *"Because of the increase of wickedness the love of most will grow cold, but the one who stands firm to the end will be saved."* With attitudes of resentment caused by conspiracy theories fantasized through imagined betrayals and the tolerance of immorality streaming through the hearts of an extremely autonomous culture, you have allowed the walls of your masterpiece to be shattered into pieces, comfortable with the convenience of hiding behind the only wall left barely standing. You both must commit to strengthening your angling views of God's working power to help in the heavily layered realms of your separate realities if you believe there is any hope to rebuild and secure again the ruined walls that protected the ever-abiding presence of God's Love residing in the oneness that made it impossible for the enemy of offense to make distinctions that might separate you from a path God destined for you both to walk down together.

This last area of concentration to be discussed is the quality of the lenses used to verify the truths shared between the images projected through its view and the convicted life these images walk in as perceived through the singularity of the lenses eye. It identified the weak links in your three-fold cord that you allowed to invade the sacredness of your union with a subliminal message that cut off almost all of the life in whatever line you have left. I have, therefore, been awarded the unprivileged opportunity of reintroducing you, Mr. and Mrs. Superhero Lover, to Offense and Resentment, the icebergs that unexpectedly hit your relationship and are just about through with sinking your love's Titanic. Your love's Titanic, once considered indestructible, like the 1912 supposedly unsinkable ship itself, was observed through the undeveloped lenses of your prematurity which arrogantly entitled you both to the wondrous luxuries of love without the patience of contentment to address the possibilities of its flaws. Now your ship that you naively said and came to believe, "Not even God Himself could sink this ship," is sinking fast in the freezing cold waters that have chilled the heat of your love's consuming fire.

For the majority of your marriage, you have elected to chastise those undisclosed flaws, violently erupting onto the canvased surface of your pictured perfection, with offenses clothed in the garments of pride stained with the fresh blood of wounds that hurt too much to heal. After further investigation, however, I discovered that approximately eighty plus percent of the offenses you have expected one another to answer for are either self-afflicted or nonexistent offenses you imagined in the unforgiving demeanor of your victimized mind. It is extremely difficult to return the responsibility of an offense, committed against you, back into the court of its offender, when both the offended and offender are the same person—you. You have brought offenses against yourselves, and your immaturity has caused you to blame one another, to excuse yourselves from the responsibility of any involvement in the attempted murder of your marriage, and your suicide.

Because of the ease of influencing your victim mentality, pride has clothed the true condition of your hearts with a story you've co-authored and penned with the achievements of your success, suppressing a suffocating bitterness triggered by a sustained resentment you honestly have no legitimate grounds for having against each other. Resentment looks to find problems in places where no problems can be found and is capable of creating a problem, just to argue, even when there is no problem to argue about. Most of your resentment is birthed in the perversely unfulfilled fantasy of your self-absorbed imagination that has indirectly caused you to blame all of your offenses on a lover that continues choosing to walk beside you, instead of on the insecurities of your most consistent offender, you yourself.

Unfortunately, the image you have chosen to brand yourselves with is dressed to impress, clothed in the outer garments of perfection's masterful design, while at the same time walking around in the smelly undergarments of an unclean lover's disgust with the burdensome task of airing out laundry, they are ashamed to clean. The fragrance of your pictured love echoes the sweet smell of Magnolia blossoms from a distance, but as you draw closer to bask in the joy of its aroma, it moves out-siders to stand disappointed after discovering that the idea of love without God stinks. The valued worth of your marriage is diminishing because of all the bags of trash you have refused to dump out, laying up in the rooms of your relationship, causing your residence to be deemed uninhabitable due to all the maggots eating away at the real issues you have refused to put in the dumpster. You are still filled with a false sense of entitlement that declares for you your rights to walk in a pictured perfection in shoes ten sizes too big for you guys to anchor your fused souls in, hoping to experience perfections success through the eyes of its grace.

So when it comes to the transparency of your pictured perfection to determine if it is a distorted perception of an image you created or the natural reflection of a masterpiece God pictured perfect, Mr. and Mrs. Lover, the lie detector test reveals your picture is flawed, gracefully framed in the perfection of God's form and bound by the chokehold of unsecured imperfections that hinder you from walking in the power that demonstrates its unfailing love. Even though God destined for the two of you to always and forever be, the consummation of every marriage bathing in the bathtub of destiny's zealous passion is dependent upon your choosing whether or not to conform your will over to the desire of the blueprint God specifically designed to guarantee Destiny's success in your marital arrangement. Yes, as of now your perfect picture looks like a rip-off, but it is possessed with an undiscovered potential to walk in the pictured perfection residing under loads of trash bags infested with maggots eating away at the flesh that covers your untied souls. Therefore, the changing of the guard is left up to the two of you.

If you're waiting for me to provide you with a one for all remedy that will easily allow you to access a comforting resolve that frees you from the consequences of your ill will towards one another, then you most certainly should be prepared for disappointment. Yes, of course, I could have bid you farewell with the misunderstanding of a proverbial cliché that temporarily stops the bleeding by declaring to your ears without any concern for the condition of your heart, that "Jesus is da way my brodah.' The truth is Jesus is the only answer to every problem every couple face, but because every marriage is unique in its own right, Jesus' way is strategically curved to fit the genetic profile of married participants on a case-by-case basis. Your marital success will not be determined by a one size fits all model but through your understanding of how God has elected to differentiate His instruction to fit you within the context of the reality you've experienced together. Differentiation provides couples with different ways of effectively addressing their personal marital dilemmas with methods that have proven to be the most accommodating to the learning styles of two united lovers. Always remember only to use the tools God gave you to fix your relationship, without digging in the toolboxes of other couples that have been granted tools only strong enough to fix their love engine.

So, choosing to love, or to love each no more, is not left up to chance, but up to the daily devotedness of your wills choosing to love each other unconditionally. If either of you would so choose to throw in the towel and walk away from a love destined, then the excellence of your beginning and the tragedy of your middle will be unfulfilled without the reward of perseverance waiting for you at your story's end. Time is an unfolding of a story in the earth that God has already written and told in heaven. Now it's time for you both to finish retelling your story in the singularity of the one-mindedness God thought to perfect the picture of the characters He still expects you to play in His story. Will you allow your love to be erased from the chronicled records of the earth's memory, or will the light of your love's embrace burn deep down in the unity of your reconciliation?

So, what will it be? Do you, Mr. and Mrs. Lover, choose to LOVE each other or LOVE each other NO MORE?

Other Books by the Author

The Superhero Chronicles

The Wounded Leader
(ISBN 978-0-615-65497-3)

The Superhero's Tell All Exclusive Interview
(ISBN 978-0-692-02244-3)

The Superhero Lover
(ISBN 978-0-692-77960-6)

Available from the author, in retail stores, on www.amazon.com and www.barnesandnoble.com, and wherever books are sold.

Contact Information

To inquire about Pastor Shaun Saunders speaking, ministering, or doing book signings and discussions at your event, you may contact him by sending an email to:

ssaunders89@yahoo.com

Connect with him on Twitter:

@ssaundersauthor

Printed in the USA
CPSIA information can be obtained
at www.ICGtesting.com
JSHW010721240324
59620JS00011B/119